2014

Medical Coding Training: CPC®
Practical Application Workbook

AAPC
Advancing the Business of Healthcare

Disclaimer

This course was current when it was published. Every reasonable effort has been made to assure the accuracy of the information within these pages. The ultimate responsibility lies with readers to ensure they are using the codes, and following applicable guidelines, correctly. AAPC employees, agents, and staff make no representation, warranty, or guarantee that this compilation of information is error-free, and will bear no responsibility or liability for the results or consequences of the use of this course. This guide is a general summary that explains guidelines and principles in profitable, efficient healthcare organizations.

Clinical Examples Used in this Book

AAPC believes it is important in training and testing to reflect as accurate a coding setting as possible to students and examinees. All examples and case studies used in our study guides, exams, and workbooks are *actual, redacted* office visit and procedure notes donated by AAPC members.

To preserve the *real world* quality of these notes for educational purposes, we have not re-written or edited the notes to the stringent grammatical or stylistic standards found in the text of our products. Some minor changes have been made for clarity or to correct spelling errors originally in the notes, but essentially they are as one would find them in a coding setting.

US Government Rights

This product includes CPT®, which is commercial technical data and/or computer data bases and/or commercial computer software and/or commercial computer software documentation, as applicable, which was developed exclusively at private expense by the American Medical Association, 515 North State Street, Chicago, Illinois, 60610. U.S. Government rights to use, modify, reproduce, release, perform, display, or disclose these technical data and/or computer data bases and/or computer software and/or computer software documentation are subject to the limited rights restrictions of DFARS 252.227-7015(b)(2) (November 1995), as applicable, for U.S. Department of Defense procurements and the limited rights restrictions of FAR 52.227-14 (June 1987) and/or subject to the restricted rights provision of FAR 52.227-14 (June 1987) and FAR 52.227-19 (June 1987), as applicable, and any applicable agency FAR Supplements, for non-Department of Defense Federal procurements.

AMA Disclaimer

CPT® copyright 2013 American Medical Association. All rights reserved.

Fee schedules, relative value units, conversion factors and/or related components are not assigned by the AMA, are not part of CPT®, and the AMA is not recommending their use. The AMA does not directly or indirectly practice medicine or dispense medical services. The AMA assumes no liability for data contained or not contained herein.

CPT® is a registered trademark of the American Medical Association.

© 2013 AAPC

2480 South 3850 West, Suite B, Salt Lake City, Utah 84120

800-626-CODE (2633), Fax 801-236-2258, www.aapc.com

Updated 110513. All rights reserved.

ISBN 978-1-626880-023; (Bundle) 978-1-626880-764

CPC®, CPC-H®, CPC-P®, CIRCC®, CPMA®, CPCO™, and CPPM® are trademarks of AAPC.

Acknowledgements

Authors:
Katherine Abel, CPC, CPB, CPMA, CPC-I
Debra A. Apfel, RN, BA, CPC, CPMA
Carrie Bosela, CPC, CPC-I
Rhonda Buckholtz, CPC, CPC-I, CPMA, CGSC, CPEDC, COBGC, CENTC
Marcella Bucknam, CPC, CPC-H, CPC-P, CPC-I, CCC, COBGC
Shelly Cronin, CPC, CPMA, CPPM, CPC-I, CANPC, CGIC, CGSC
Kelly Dennis, CPC, CPC-I, CANPC
Mary Divine, CPC, CPC-H, CPC-I, CUC
Brad Ericson, MPC, CPC, COSC
Raemarie Jimenez, CPC, CPB, CPMA, CPC-I CANPC, CRHC
Betty Hovey, CPC, CPC-H, CPB, CPMA, CPC-I, CPCD
Dolly Perrine, CPC, CPMA, CPC-I, CUC
Jean Pryor, CPC, CPMA, CPC-I, CIMC
Dorothy Steed, CPC-H, CPCO, CPMA, CPC-I, CEMC, CFPC
Kate Tierney, CPC, CPC-P, CPMA, CEDC, CEMC, CGSC, COBGC
G. John Verhovshek, MA, CPC
Susan Ward, CPC, CPC-H, CPC-I, CEMC, CPCD, CPRC

Reviewers:
Lynn Anderanin, CPC, CPC-I, COSC
Nicole Benjamin, CPC, CPC-I, CEDC
Glade B. Curtis, MD, MPH, FACOG, CPC, CPPM, CPC-I, COBGC
Jennifer Hume, CPC, CPCO, CPMA, CEMC
Lindsay-Anne McDonald Jenkins, CPC, CPC-H, CPC-I, CPMA, CANPC, CIRCC, RN, CRNA (retired)
Vandna Kejariwal, CPC, CPC-H, CPMA, CPC-I, CEDC
Barbara Pross, CPC, CPMA, CPC-I, CEDC, CEMC, COBGC
Carrie Lynn Rawlings, CPC, CPMA, CPC-I, CCVTC, CEMC
Alice Reybitz, RN, BA, CPC, CPC-H, CPC-I
Carrie Severson, CPC, CPC-H, CPMA, CPC-I
Kathy Skolnick, CPC, CPCO, CPMA, CPC-I
Charleen Yamasato, CPC, CPC-I

Production:
Dianne Allred, Designer, Desktop Publishing
Tina M. Smith, Desktop Publishing

AAPC   www.aapc.com   iii

Contents

Exercise 1

1. What type of profession might a skilled coder enter?

2. What is the difference between outpatient and inpatient coding?

3. What is a mid-level provider?

4. Discuss the different parts of Medicare and what each program covers.

5. Evaluation and management services are often provided in a standard format such as SOAP. What does SOAP represent?

6. What are five tips for coding operative reports?

7.   What is medical necessity and what tool can you refer to for the medical
     necessity of a service?

8.   What are some common reasons Medicare may deny a procedure or service?

9.   Under the Privacy Rule, the minimum necessary standard does not apply to
     what type of disclosures?

10. What are the seven key actions of an internal compliance plan?

1. Diagnosis: Calcification left basal ganglia.

   Where are the basal ganglia located?

2. Diagnosis: Vesicoureteral reflux.

   What is this a reflux of?

3. Documentation: The posterior vaginal fornix and outer cervical os were prepped with a cleansing solution.

   In this statement, what does "os" stand for?

4. Hysterosalpingogram report: "Right cornual contour abnormality."

   What is the cornua referred to?

5. Surgical Procedure: Myringotomy

What anatomic location is being operated on?

6. Documentation: There was no cleft of the uvula or sub mucosal palate by visual and palpable exam.

What is being examined?

7. Documentation: Recession of left inferior rectus muscle, 5 mm.

What anatomic location is being operated on?

8. Diagnosis: Kyphosis

What anatomic location does this diagnosis refer to?

9. Documentation: Suprapatellar recess showed no evidence of loose bodies or joint pathology.

What anatomic location does this refer to?

10. Colles' Fracture

What anatomic location does this refer to?

AAPC

www.aapc.com

2.3

Exercise 1

Directions: Using the ICD-9-CM codebook, locate the diagnosis codes for the following conditions.

1. Fever

2. Migraine headache

3. Otitis Media

4. Epigastric pain

5. Acute asthma exacerbation

6. Acute myocardial infarction

7. Hypertensive heart disease

8. Syncope

9. Nausea and vomiting

10. GERD

11. Chlamydia infection

12. Sickle cell anemia

13. Rupture spleen

14. Cellulitis of the arm

15. Lung mass

16. H1N1 flu

17. Uncontrolled diabetes with diabetic glaucoma

18. Left cheek abrasion

19. Cholecystitis

20. Eyebrow laceration

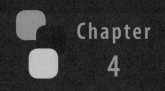

Case 1

Operative Report

Preoperative Diagnoses: Splenic abscess and multiple intra-abdominal abscess, related to HIV, AIDS, and hepatitis C.

Postoperative Diagnoses: Splenic abscess and multiple intra-abdominal abscess, related to HIV, AIDS, and hepatitis C.

Operative Procedure:

1. Exploratory laparotomy with drainage of multiple intra-abdominal abscesses.

2. Splenectomy.

3. Vac Pak closure.

Findings: This is a 42-year-old man who was recently admitted to the Medical Service with a splenic defect and found to have a splenic vein thrombosis. He was treated with antibiotics and anticoagulation. He returned and was admitted with a CT scan showing mass of left upper quadrant abscess surrounding both sides of the spleen, as well as multiple other intra-abdominal abscesses below the left lobe of the liver in both lower quadrants and in the pelvis. The patient has a psychiatric illness and was difficult to consent and had been anticoagulated with an INR of 3. Once those issues were resolved by psychiatry consult and phone consent from the patient's father, he was brought to the operating room.

Operative Procedure: The patient was brought to operating room, and a time-out procedure was performed. He was already receiving parenteral antibiotics. He was placed in the supine position and then under general endotracheal anesthetic. Anesthesia started multiple IVs and an arterial line. A Foley catheter was sterilely inserted with some difficulty requiring a Coude catheter. After the abdomen was prepped and draped in the sterile fashion, a long midline incision was made through the skin. This was carried through the subcutaneous tissues and down through the midline fascia using the Bovie. The fascia was opened in the midline. The entire left upper quadrant was replaced with an abscess peel separate from the free peritoneal cavity, this was opened, and at least 3 to 4 L of foul smelling crankcase colored fluid was removed. Once the abscess cavity was completely opened, it was evident that the spleen was floating within this pus as had been predicted by the CT. This was irrigated copiously and the left lower quadrant subhepatic and pelvic abscesses were likewise discovered containing the same foul smelling dark bloody fluid. All of these areas were sucked out, irrigated, and the procedure repeated multiple times.

 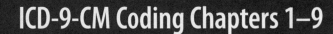

At this point, we thought it reasonable to go ahead with the splenectomy. The anatomic planes were obviously terribly distorted. There was no clear margin between stomach spleen, colon spleen, etc, but most of the dense attachments were to the abscess cavity peel. Using this as a guide, the spleen was eventually rotated up and out to the point where the upper attachments presumably where the short gastrics used to reside were taken via Harmonic scalpel. The single fire of a 45 mm stapler with vascular load was taken across the lower pole followed by 2 firings of the echelon stapler across the hilum. This controlled most of the ongoing bleeding. Single bleeding site below the splenic artery was controlled with 2 stitches, one of 3-0 Prolene and the other of 4-0 Prolene. Because of diffuse ooze in the area and the fact that the patient would be scheduled for a return visit to the operating room tomorrow to reinspect the abscess cavities, it was elected to leave two laparotomy pads in the left upper quadrant and Vac Pak the abdomen. The Vac Pak was created using blue towels and Ioban dressings in the usual fashion with 10 mm fully perforated flat Jackson-Pratt drains brought out at the appropriate level. The patient was critical throughout the procedure and will be taken directly to the Intensive Care Unit, intubated, with a plan for re-exploration and removal of the packs tomorrow. The patient received 4 units of packed cells during the procedure, as well as, albumin and a large volume of crystalloid. There were no intraoperative complications noted and the specimen sent included the spleen. Cultures from the abscess cavity were also taken.

What diagnosis/es code(s) are reported?

Case 2

Dear Dr. Smith,

Mr. Martin was seen in the office for continued management of his breast cancer. He's having some increasing pain in his breast which is due to the cancer. He is also complaining of neck pain. It does not seem to be worse at night; it seems to be worse with activity. He has no other symptoms. Otherwise his review of systems is unremarkable. He's had no constitutional symptoms.

On physical exam, he is alert and oriented. Eyes: EOMI, PERLA, no icterus. The heart had a regular rate and rhythm, S1, S2 within normal limits. The lungs are clear to auscultation and percussion. The abdomen was soft, without masses or organomegaly. He was tender to palpation over the left anterior iliac crest where he had previously been radiated. Otherwise, he had no point tenderness over his musculoskeletal system. Neck: Supple. No tenderness, no enlarged lymph nodes in the neck.

Assessment: Adenocarcinoma of the left breast, stage IV, positive estrogen receptor status; Neck pain

Plan: The plan is to continue the Tamoxifen at this time. His laboratory studies were reviewed and were essentially unremarkable; however, we'll obtain bone scan to ascertain the extent of his disease.

Sincerely,

John Smith, M.D.

What diagnosis/es code(s) are reported?

Case 3

Subjective: Low-grade fever at home. She has had some lumps in the abdominal wall and when she injects her insulin, it does seem to hurt there. She stopped four of her medications including Neurontin, Depakote, Lasix, and Premarin, and overall she feels quite well. Unfortunately, she has put on 20 pounds since our last visit.

Objective:

Heent: Tympanic membranes are retracted but otherwise clear. The nose shows significant green rhinorrhea present. Throat mildly inflamed with moderate postnasal drainage.

NECK: No significant adenopathy.

LUNGS: Clear.

HEART: Regular rate and rhythm.

ABDOMEN: Soft, obese, and nontender. Multiple lipomas are palpated.

Assessment

1. Diabetes mellitus, type I.
2. Diabetic neuropathy.
3. Acute sinusitis.

Plan: At this time I have recommended the addition of some Keflex for her acute sinusitis. I have given her a chair for the shower. They will not cover her Glucerna anymore so a note for that will be required.

What diagnosis/es code(s) are reported?

Case 4

S: The patient presents today for reevaluation and titration of carvedilol for his coronary artery disease and hyperlipidemia. His weight is up 7 pounds. He has quit smoking. He has no further cough and he states he is feeling well except for the weight gain. He states he doesn't feel he's eating more but his wife does state that he's eating more. We've been attempting to titrate up his carvedilol to 25 mg twice a day from initially the 6.25. He has tolerated the titration quite well. He does get cephalgias on occasion. He states he has a weak spell but this is before he takes his morning medicine. I did update his medical list here today. I did give him samples of Lipitor.

O: Weight is 217, pulse rate 68, respirations 16, and blood pressure 138/82. HEENT examination is unchanged. His heart is a regular rate. His lungs are clear.

A: 1. CAD

2. Hyperlipidemia

P: 1. The plan is samples of Lipitor for two months' supply that I have.

2. We've increased his Coreg to 25 mg bid. He'll recheck with us in six months.

What diagnosis/es code(s) are reported?

Case 5

Preoperative Diagnosis: Bilateral profound sensorineural hearing loss.

Postoperative Diagnosis: Bilateral profound sensorineural hearing loss.

Procedures Performed:

1. Placement of left nucleus cochlear implant.

2. Facial nerve monitoring for an hour.

3. Microscope use.

Anesthesia: General.

Indications: This is a 69-year-old woman who has had progressive hearing loss over the last 10–15 years. Hearing aids are not useful for her. She is a candidate for cochlear implant by FDA standards. The risks, benefits, and alternatives of procedure were described to the patient, who voiced understanding and wished to proceed.

Procedure: After properly identifying the patient, she was taken to the main operating room, where general anesthetic was induced. The table was turned to 180 degrees and a standard left-sided postauricular shave and injection of 1% lidocaine plus 1:100,000 epinephrine was performed. The patient was then prepped and draped in a sterile fashion after placing facial nerve monitoring probes, which were tested and found to be working well. At this time, the previously outlined incision line was incised and flaps were elevated. A subtemporal pocket was designed in the usual fashion for placement of the device. A standard cortical mastoidectomy was then performed and the fascial recess was opened exposing the area of the round window niche. The lip of the round window was drilled down exposing the round window membrane. At this time, the wound was copiously irrigated with Bacitracin containing solution and the device was then placed into the pocket. A 1 mm cochleostomy was then made and the device was then inserted into the cochleostomy with an advance-off stylet technique. A small piece of temporalis muscle was then packed around the cochleostomy and the wound was then closed in layers using 3-0 and 4–0 Monocryl and Steri-Strips. A standard mastoid dressing was applied. The patient was returned to the anesthesia, where she was awakened, extubated, and taken to the recovery room in stable condition.

What diagnosis/es code(s) are reported?

Case 6

Preoperative diagnosis: Cataract. Left eye

Postoperative diagnosis: Cataract. Left eye, Presbyopia

Procedure:

1. Cataract extraction with IOL implant

2. Correction of presbyopia with lens implantation

Procedure detail: The patient was brought to the Operating Room under neuroleptic anesthesia monitoring. A topical anesthetic was placed within the operative eye and the patient was prepped and draped in usual manner for sterile ophthalmic surgery A lid speculum was inserted in the right infrapalpebral space. A 6-0 silk suture was placed through the episclera at 12 o'clock. A subconjunctival injection of non-preserved lidocaine was given. A peritomy was fashioned from 11 o'clock to 1 o'clock with Westcott scissors. Hemostasis was achieved with the wet-field cauter. A 3 mm incision was made in the cornea and dissected anteriorly with a crescent blade The anterior chamber was entered at 12 o'clock and 2 o'clock with a Supersharp blade. A non-preserved lidocaine was instilled into the anterior chamber. Viscoelastic was instilled in the anterior chamber and using a bent 25-gauge needle, a 360 degree anterior capsulotomy was performed using an Utrata forceps. The capsulotomy was measured and found to be 5.5 mm in diameter. Using an irrigating cannula, the lens nucleus was hydrodissected and loosened. Using the phacoemulsification unit, the lens nucleus was divided and emulsified. The irrigating/aspirating tip was used to remove the cortical fragments from the capsular bag and the posterior capsule was polished. Using a curette to polish the anterior capsule, cortical fragments were removed from the anterior lens capsule for 270 degrees The irrigating/aspirating tip was used to remove the capsular fragments. The anterior chamber and capsule bag were inflated with viscoelastic and using a lens inserter, a Cystalens was then placed within the capsular bag and rotated to the horizontal position. The viscoelastic was removed with the irrigating/aspirating tip and the lens was found to be in excellent position with a slight posterior vault. The wound was hydrated with balanced salt solution and tested and found to be watertight at a pressure of 20 mm Hg. Topical Vigainox was applied. The conjunctiva was repositioned over the wound with a wet field cautery. The traction suture and lid speculum were removed. A patch was applied. The patient tolerated the procedure well and left the Operating Room in good condition.

What diagnosis/es code(s) are reported?

Case 7

Progress note

This patient is a 50-year-old female who began developing bleeding, bright red blood per rectum, approximately two weeks ago. She is referred by her family physician. She states that after a bowel movement she noticed blood in the toilet. She denied any prior history of bleeding or pain with defecation. She states that she has had an external hemorrhoid that did bleed at times but that is not where this bleeding is coming from. She is presently concerned because a close friend of hers was recently diagnosed with rectal carcinoma requiring chemotherapy that was missed by her primary doctor. She is here today for evaluation for a colonoscopy.

Physical examination, she appears a well appearing, 50-year-old, white female. Abdomen is soft, nontender, nondistended.

Assessment: 50-year-old female with rectal bleeding

Plan: We'll schedule the patient for an outpatient colonoscopy. The patient was made aware of all the risks involved with the procedure and was willing to proceed.

What diagnosis/es code(s) are reported?

Case 8

Subjective: Here to follow up on her atrial fibrillation. No new problems. Feeling well. Medications are per medication sheet. These were reconstituted with the medications that she was discharged home on.

Objective: Blood pressure is 110/64. Pulse is regular at 72. Neck is supple. Chest is clear. Cardiac normal sinus rhythm.

Assessment: Atrial fibrillation, currently stable.

Plan:

1. Prothrombin time to monitor long term use of anticoagulant.

2. Follow up with myself in 1 month, sooner as needed if has any other problems in the meantime. Will also check a creatinine and potassium today as well.

What diagnosis/es code(s) are reported?

Case 9

Follow-up visit: The patient has some memory problems. She is hard of hearing. She is legally blind. Her pharmacist and her family are very worried about her memory issues. She lives at home, family takes care of laying out her medications and helping with the chores but she does take care of her own home to best of her ability.

Exam: Pleasant elderly woman in no acute distress. She has postop changes of her eyes. TMs are dull. Pharynx is clear. Neck is supple without adenopathy. Lungs are clear. Good air movement. Heart is regular. She had a slight murmur. Abdomen is soft. Moderately obese. Nontender. Extremities no clubbing or edema. Foot exam shows some bunion deformity but otherwise healthy as consequence. Light touch is preserved. There is no ankle edema or stasis change. Examination of the upper arms reveal good range of motion. There is significant pain in her shoulder with rotational movements. It localized mostly over the deltoid. There is no other deformity. There is a very slight left shoulder discomfort and slight right hip discomfort.

Impression:
1. Type 2 diabetes good control. Most recent A1C done today 5.9%. Liver test normal. Cholesterol 199, LDL a little high at 115.
2. Right shoulder pain.
3. Benign hypertensive cardiovascular disease.
4. Dementia

Plans:
1. I offered her and her family neuropsych eval to evaluate for dementia. Her system complex is consistent with dementia whether it be from small vascular disease or Alzheimer's is unknown. At this point they much rather initiate treatment than go through an exhaustive neuropysch test.
2. For the shoulder we decided on right deltoid bursa aspiration injection. She has had injection for bursitis in the past and prefers to go this route. She will ice and rest the shoulder after injection.
3. Follow up in 3 months.

Procedure: Aspiration injection right deltoid bursa. The point of maximal tenderness was identified, skin was prepped with alcohol. A 25-gauge 1 ½-inch needle was advanced to the humerus and then aspirated. 1 cc of 0.25% Marcaine mixed with 80 mg Depomedrol was deposited. Needle withdrawn. Band-Aid applied. Post injection she had marked improvement, increased range of motion consistent with good placement of the medication. She was started on cerefolin plus NAC and Aricept starter pack was given with email away script. Follow up in 3 months and we will reassess her dementia at that time.

What diagnosis/es code(s) are reported?

Case 10

CC: HTN

Interval history: No new complaints.

Exam: NAD. 130/80, 84, 22. Lungs are clear. Heart RRR, no MRGs. Abdomen is soft, non-tender. No peripheral edema.

Impression: Stable HTN on current meds. He also has mild OA for which he takes PRN MOTRIN.

Plan: No changes needed. RTC in six months with labs.

What diagnosis/es code(s) are reported?

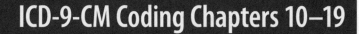

Case 1

Reason for consult: Acute Renal Failure

HPI: Patient followed in the past by my associate for CKD with baseline creatinine of 1.8 two weeks ago. Found to have severe ARF this morning associated with acidosis and moderate hyperkalemia after presenting to the ER with "dehydration." The patient is currently admitted under observation status to the hospitalist service and the renal team is called for a consult.

ROS: Cardiovascular: Negative for CP/PND. GI: Negative for nausea; positive for diarrhea. GU: Negative for obstructive symptoms or documented exposure to nephrotoxins. All other systems reviewed and are negative.

PFSH: Negative family history of hereditary renal disease and negative history of tobacco or ETOH abuse.

Exam: Constitutional: 99/52, 18, 102. NAD. Conversant. EYES: anicteric sclerae, no proptosis, PERRL. ENMT: Normal aside from somewhat dry mucus membranes. CARDIOVASCULAR: RRR, no MRGs, no edema. RESPIRATORY: Lungs CTA, normal respiratory effort. GI: NABS, no HSM. SKIN: Warm and dry, decreased turgor. PSYCHIATRIC: A&OX3 with appropriate affect.

Labs: BUN 99, creatinine 3.6, HCO3 14, K 5.9.

Impression

1. New, acute renal failure, due to dehydration
2. Underlying stage III CKD
3. Mild hypotension

Plan

1. Bolus with another liter of NS wide open.
2. Then start D5W with 3 amps of HCO3 at 150 cc/hr.
3. Repeat labs in eight hours.
4. Further diagnostic testing will be ordered if no improvement with volume repletion.

What diagnosis/es code(s) are reported?

Case 2

Progress Note

Chief Complaint: Multiple Ulcers

S: Jane returns, accompanied by her caregiver, who states that she believes the ulcers have gotten "about as good as they are going to." The edema of the leg seems to be much better controlled.

O: Exam reveals marked improvement of the edema of both lower legs, right better than left. All of the ulcers are now extremely superficial and seem to almost be partial thickness skin. There is no cellulitis. The only uncomfortable area seems to be on the sole of the left foot where there is considerable bony abnormality and/or tophaceous deposits which have distorted the bottom of her foot dramatically. In order to relieve foot pain, a sole nerve block posterior to the lateral malleolus is carried out with a 50:50 mixture of 1% Lidocaine with epinephrine and .5% Marcaine. Following this she gets good relief from the pain of the lateral posterior part of the foot. The legs are cleansed with Hibiclens and multi-layer compression wraps are reapplied by Samuel Myers, PA.

A: Ulcers on the feet. Edema in the lower extremities. Foot pain treated with nerve block. Fantastic course to date thanks to her caregiver.

P: Continue with wound care as before, return to the office in six to eight weeks at which time assuming everything is going well we could set up an OR time for panniculectomy. She appears to understand and is willing to proceed.

What diagnosis/es code(s) are reported?

Case 3

S: The patient presents today after having a cabinet fall on her. She states that the people that put in the cabinet missed the stud by about two inches. The patient complains of cephalgias, primarily occipital, extending up into the bilateral occipital and parietal regions. The patient denies any vision changes, any taste changes, any smell changes. The patient has marked amount of tenderness across the superior trapezius.

O: Her weight is 188, which is up 5 pounds from last time, blood pressure 144/82, pulse rate 70, respirations are 18. She has full strength in her upper extremities. DTRs in the biceps and triceps are adequate. Grip strength is adequate. Heart is a regular rate. Lungs are clear.

A:

1. Cephalgia

2. Thoracic somatic dysfunction

P: The plan at this time is to send her for physical therapy three times a week times, four weeks for cervical soft tissue muscle massage, as well as upper dorsal. We'll recheck her in one month.

What diagnosis/es code(s) are reported?

Case 4

Chief Complaint: Right shoulder injury.

Mode of Arrival: Private vehicle.

History of Present Illness: The patient is a 59-year-old male who states that just prior to arrival he was going into a supermarket when the revolving door suddenly slammed on him. It caught him across the right side of his chest anteriorly and posteriorly. He was unable to liberate himself from the door and an employee had to help him out. He denies any current shortness of breath though did say he had the wind knocked out of him. He complains of pain in the anterior and posterior chest wall, posteriorly medial to the scapula. He denies any numbness, tingling, or weakness in his left arm however he does state that it seems to be painful and difficult for him to either lift or even drop his arm. He again denies any numbness, tingling, or weakness distally. He denies any injury to his head or neck though he did have a temporary episode of spasms on the left side of his neck. He has not taken anything for pain.

Review of systems: Negative for fevers, chills, or unintentional weight loss. No neck pain, numbness, tingling, weakness, nausea, vomiting, shortness of breath, hemoptysis, or cough. All other systems reviewed and negative except as noted.

Physical Examination:

General: The patient is awake and alert, lying comfortably in the treatment bed. He is nontoxic in appearance.

Vital signs: Temperature 98 3, pulse 81, respirations 16, blood pressure 134/81, pulse oximetry 95% on room air.

HEENT: The head is normocephalic and Atraumatic.

Neck: Nontender to palpation in the posterior midline. The trachea is midline. There is no subcutaneous emphysema. There is no tenderness over the paraspinous muscles.

Heart: Regular rate and rhythm without murmurs.

Lungs: Clear to auscultation bilaterally without wheezes, crackles or rhonchi. The chest wall does expand symmetrically.

Thorax/Chest wall: Demonstrates mild tenderness anteriorly and demonstrates distinct tenderness posteriorly along the medial aspect of the scapula. No bruising or ecchymosis is noted on the skin of the chest wall. Patient keeps his right shoulder lowered. There is no deformity noted. There is no tenderness over the right clavicle. No bony deformity is noted there. There is no subcutaneous emphysema of the chest wall.

Extremities: Warm and dry without clubbing, cyanosis, or edema. Grip strength is 5/5 bilaterally. Patient can flex and extend all fingers without difficulty. He can pronate and supinate at the elbow. He does complain of pain in the shoulder when he flexes and extends at the elbow. Normal radial and ulnar pulses are appreciated in the bilateral upper extremities. Capillary refill is brisk. Sensation is normal in all nerve distributions in the bilateral arms.

Abdomen: Soft, nondistended. Nontender.

Diagnostics: Two views of the chest, PA and lateral, and three views of the right shoulder were obtained. ED COURSE: The patient received a total of 2 mg of Dilaudid for pain, 1 mg of sublingual Ativan. His arm was placed in a sling. This was well tolerated and the patient was discharged home.

Medical decision making: It appears the patient has an anterior chest wall and a posterior chest wall contusion. The exact reasoning why he has so much difficulty moving the shoulder is unclear at this time as he is completely neurologically intact from what I can tell. He can adduct and abduct at the shoulder as I have seen him do it as he was moving around to be examined. X-rays demonstrate no evidence of fracture or dislocation. At this point I am going to discharge the patient home, have him use ice packs, doing prescriptions for pain medications and have him return for any new or worsening symptoms.

Impression:

1. Anterior and posterior chest wall contusion.

2. Right shoulder injury.

Plan: Discharge home. Return for new or worsening symptoms. Sling for comfort.

What diagnosis/es code(s) are reported?

Case 5

HPI: 20-year-old female, estimated gestational age 25.3 weeks, who presents with red staining after wiping with toilet paper this afternoon. No abdominal pain. Contractions: Negative; Fetal Movement: Present

ROS:

Constitutional: Negative

Headache: Negative

Urinary: Negative

Nausea: Negative

Vomiting: Negative

Past medical/Family/Social history:

Medical history: Negative

Surgical history: Negative

Social history: Alcohol: Denies; Tobacco: Denies; Drugs: Denies

Exam:

General appearance: No Acute Distress

Abdominal: Soft. Nontender

Vagina: Blood Clots size: 1.5 cm and amount 2.Discharge: Pink
No Hyphae, BV or TRICH and CX not irritated

Cervix: Deffered

Uterus: Fundal Height: 24 cm

MDM: Labs: FFN, UA R+M, C+S, GC/Chlamydia, CBC, Type and RH, DAU
Labs reviewed and WNL

Ultrasound: Negative for placenta previa

Notes: Pt continues with contractions mildly, but does not feel it. Pt given Celestone I/M. D/C and to return tomorrow for repeat Celestone injection.

Diagnosis: Threatened Premature Labor

What diagnosis/es code(s) are reported?

Case 6

Office Note:

RE: Injection, strapping of foot and ankle.

Chief complaint: heel pain, 6 months' duration. No inflammation, no heat.

Diagnosis: Heel spur.

Treatment: Weight reduction, injection of Celestone, Xylocaine plain, Pulses good, DTR, vibration and temp normal

Orthotics suggested, better shoes suggested. Lawyer by trade. Criminal trial attorney. Referred by his partner. Discussed diet, orthotic shoes. Return if need be in 61 days.

What diagnosis/es code(s) are reported?

Case 7

Preoperative diagnosis:

1. 2 cm transverse laceration of right forehead.

2. 3 cm stellate laceration of right upper eyelid.

3. 3 cm trap door laceration of right lower eyelid.

Operative diagnosis:

Operation performed: multiple layer closure of above lacerations totalling 8 cm.

Anesthesia: Local.

Preoperative note: This patient is a 64-year-old white female. She has a very difficult time ambulating, doing so with a walker and intermittently sitting. This evening, unfortunately, she fell from her motorized wheelchair and struck the right side of her forehead. She was brought to the emergency department where she was thoroughly evaluated by Dr. Tim and is in the process of getting C-spine films and is accordingly in a cervical spine support. I was called to evaluate and treat these lacerations due to their extensive and complex nature. The lacerations are as described above. Forehead laceration is linear, deep but otherwise uneventful. The upper right eyelid laceration is approximately 3 cm in length and the medial aspect of it is somewhat dusky because it is very thin and devoid of vasculature. The lower eyelid laceration is trap door and somewhat deep. It also becomes very thin at the medial aspect. However, there appear to be no duskiness. It seems to be well vascularized. In any event, we chose to immediately repair these with local anesthesia.

Details of operative procedure: Approximately a total of 6 ml of 2% lidocaine with 1:100,000 epinephrine was then infiltrated into the three wounds. They were then thoroughly cleansed with soap and closure was begun on the upper eyelid to begin with. We used 6-0 Vicryl subcutaneous sutures to attack the flap back into position and once this was accomplished we used individual 6-0 Prolene sutures on the skin to complete the closure. Attention was then turned to the right lower eyelid laceration where essentially an identical procedure was done. The wounds were somewhat similar in that they were flaps pedicled to the lateral towards the medial. Again, 6-0 Vicryl subcutaneous and 6-0 Prolene individual skin sutures. Finally attention was turned to the forehead laceration, which was similarly closed with these same sutures, 6-0 Vicryl subcutaneous and 6-0 Prolene on the skin. The wounds were then dressed with Bacitracin ophthalmic. Patient was instructed to keep them moist at all times, do not let crust form. She was also instructed in the appropriate analgesics to be taken orally and given my office number for a follow up appointment. At the end of the procedure, she was then sent back to X-ray for CAT scan of her C-spine.

What diagnosis/es code(s) are reported?

Case 8

Preoperative diagnosis:

Right forearm radial shaft fracture with possible mild distal radioulnar joint subluxation.

Postoperative diagnosis:

Right forearm radial shaft fracture with possible mild distal radioulnar joint subluxation.

Anesthesia: Axillary block with general.

Operation: Right radius fracture open reduction and internal fixation with closed reduction distal radioulnar joint.

Indications: This is a 22-year-old male who sustained a right forearm fracture injury as indicated above and in the medical records and office notes.

Description of procedure: The patient was placed under axillary block in the holding area followed by general anesthesia in the operating room. Patient identification, correct procedure, and site were confirmed. Antibiotics were provided in an appropriate fashion preoperatively.

A dorsal/posterior approach to the fracture was performed with a standard recommended incision, location, and technique. The interval between the extensor carpi radialis brevis and extensor digitorum communis was developed. The extensor pollicis brevis and the abductor pollicis were gently retracted one way or the other to expose the fracture site and the fracture was just beneath this area. The radial sensory nerve was identified and protected throughout the procedure. The fracture was exposed with minimal soft tissue stripping. The bone holding forceps were placed on either side of the fracture and the overriding fracture was manipulated with gentle traction and manipulation and the fracture reduced. This effectively reduced the distal radioulnar joint.

A small fragment, Synthes DCP locking plate was utilized to fix the fracture. Eight holes were utilized. Due to the nature of the fracture and the anatomy, there were 3 screws distal, 4 screws proximal, and the last hole was at the area of the fracture. Initially to achieve satisfactory bone to plate contact, 3 lag screws were required and these were placed initially. This was followed by placement of the remaining screws that were utilized proximal and distal to the fracture site to be locking screws. Intraoperative X-rays utilizing the C-arm were performed throughout the procedure to guide fracture reduction and hardware replacement. Final X-rays demonstrated excellent alignment of the fracture in the distal radioulnar joint. Excellent coaptation of the bony surfaces was obtained.

Final irrigation of the wound was performed. The wound was closed in layers in a standard fashion. Splints were applied. Total tourniquet time was approximately 60 minutes. The patient tolerated the procedure well and went to recovery room in satisfactory condition. Sponge and needle count correct x2. Estimated blood loss minimal.

What diagnosis/es code(s) are reported?

Case 9

Preoperative diagnosis: Congenital hydrocephalus.

Postoperative diagnosis: Congenital hydrocephalus.

Clinical history: The patient is a 2-month-old boy who was born and was IUGR. However, did well for the first several weeks; however, then developed to have a large head. Mom noticed full fontanelle arid in the last week or so, they have noticed the eyes have decreased mobility. He tends to stare straight. Has some troubles looking up and even to the sides bilaterally. Therefore, reported to her pediatrician. Pediatrician got a CT scan and referred the patient and I saw the patient yesterday in clinic. We ordered an HRI, HRT was done this morning. PIRI shows the congenital hydrocephalus and cyst in the posterior fossa; however, it is not a Dandy-Walker. We had a discussion with the family about risks, benefits, potential complications, and also different procedures. We talked about a third ventriculostomy; however, given the patient's age and the fact it was hydrocephalus, he has elected to go with the shunt. Family are comfortable with this, bringing him to the OR today for shunting.

What diagnosis/es code(s) are reported?

Case 10

This 67-year-old Medicare patient is seen for a screening Pap and pelvic examination at our office today. She is an established patient and complaining of abnormal vaginal discharge on and off for approximately three weeks. She denied any trauma. Patient is not sexually active and her LMP was 10 years ago. She denies any chest pain, shortness of breath, or urinary problems. Patient had Pap and pelvic exam one year ago and is requesting a Pap and pelvic exam today. Patient was presented with an ABN, which was signed.

Past medical history: Two vaginal deliveries, one in 1965 and another in 1967. Allergies, unknown. Medications include Micardis 80 mg for hypertension. She does not smoke or drink. She is married and lives with her husband.

Examination: Vital Signs: BP 125/70; Pulse 85, Respirations 20. Height 5' 5", Weight 135 lb. Well developed, well nourished female in no acute distress.

HEENT: Pupils equal, round and reactive to light and accommodation. Extraocular muscles are intact:

Neck: Thyroid not palpable. No jugular distention. Carotid pulses are present bilaterally.

Breasts: Manual breast exam reveals no masses, tenderness, or nipple discharge. The breasts are asymmetrical with no nipple discharge.

Abdomen: No masses or tenderness noted. No hernias appreciated. No enlargement of the liver or spleen.

Pelvic: Vaginal examination reveals no lesions or masses. Discharge is noted and a sample was collected for testing and sent to an outside laboratory for testing. No bleeding noted. Examination of the external genitalia reveals normal pubic hair distribution. The vulva appears to be within normal limits. There are no lesions noted. A speculum is inserted. There is no evidence of prolapse. The cervix appears normal. A cervical smear is obtained and will be sent to pathology. The speculum is removed and a manual pelvic examination is performed. It appears that the uterus is smooth and no masses can be felt. Rectal examination is within normal limits. Screening occult blood is negative. Uterus is not enlarged. Urinary: Urethral meatus is normal. No masses noted for urethra or bladder.

Assessment and plan: Routine Pap and pelvic; Vaginal discharge. Patient had Pap and pelvic examination one year ago. Patient was sent to our in-house lab for blood draw today and she is to follow-up in one week for lab results.

What diagnosis/es code(s) are reported?

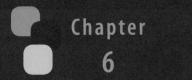

Exercise 1

Look up the procedures in the CPT® codebook and list the CPT® code. No modifiers are necessary for this exercise.

1. **Pyloroplasty**

2. **Deep biopsy of soft tissue of the ankle**

3. **Osteotomy, humerus, with internal fixation.**

4. **Renal biopsy, percutaneous, needle**

5. **Destruction of a malignant lesion on the face with a lesion diameter of 1.2 cm.**

6. Emergency endotracheal intubation

7. Measurement of spirometric forced expiratory flows, before and after bronchodilator, in an infant or child through 2 years of age.

8. An electrolyte panel performed on an 86-year-old for dizziness.

9. A frontal and lateral chest X-ray is performed in the office for a patient with chest pain.

10. The performance measure code for history obtained regarding new or changing moles.

Exercise 2

List the CPT® or HCPCS Level II modifier(s) for the definition given.

1. **Decision for surgery**

2. **Increased procedural service**

3. **Physical status modifier for a patient with a severe systemic disease**

4. **Right hand, thumb**

5. **Unrelated evaluation and management services by the same physician during a postoperative period**

6. **Staged or related procedure or service by the same physician during the post-operative period**

7. Significant, separately identifiable E/M service by the same physician on the same day of the procedure or other service

8. Left foot, great toe

9. Waiver of liability statement on file (goes with ABN)

10. Reduced Services

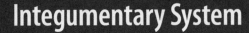
Case 1

Preoperative diagnosis: Rapidly enlarging suspicious lesion of patient's right forehead.

Postoperative diagnosis: Rapidly enlarging suspicious lesion of patient's right forehead.

Operation performed: Wide local excision with intermediate closure of right forehead.

Indications: The patient is a 78-year-old white male who recently in the last month or so noticed a rapidly enlarging suspicious lesion on the right side of his forehead.

Description of procedure: The patient was placed in the supine position on the table, was given no sedation. The area of his right forehead was prepped and draped with Betadine paint in normal sterile fashion. The area to be excised was on the right side of the patient's mid forehead. This had a maximum diameter of 1.1 cm. This had a 0.3 cm margin designed for total resection of 1.7 cm. This was infiltrated with 1% Lidocaine with Epinephrine. After waiting for hemostasis, it was excised, tagged, and sent for permanent pathology. The wound was then irrigated; several bleeders were tied off, and cauterized and closed in multiple layers with inverted dermises of 3-0 Vicryl, a running subcuticular stitch of 4-0 Vicryl and a few 5-0 chromics. The total length of this incision was 3 cm. This was covered with Steri-Strips, gauze, and tape. Patient tolerated this procedure with no complication and was sent home in stable condition.

Final diagnosis: Skin, right forehead, wide local excision, keratoacanthoma, possible squamous cell carcinoma, margins are free of tumor.

What are the CPT® and ICD-9-CM codes reported?

Case 2

Preoperative diagnosis: Basal cell carcinoma

Postoperative diagnosis: Same

Operation: Mohs Surgery

Indications: The patient has a biopsy proven basal cell carcinoma on the nasal tip measuring 8 x 7 mm. Due to its location, Mohs surgery is indicated. Mohs surgical procedure was explained including other therapeutic options, and the inherent risks of bleeding, scar formation, reaction to local anesthesia, cosmetic deformity, recurrence, infection, and nerve damage. Informed consent was obtained and the patient underwent fresh tissue Mohs surgery as follows.

STAGE I: The site of the skin cancer was identified concurrently by both the patient and Dr. and marked with a surgical pen; the margins of the excision were delineated with the marking pen. The patient was placed supine on the operating table. The wound was defined and infiltrated with 1% Lidocaine with epinephrine 1:100,000. All gross tumor was completely excised in a debulking stage using aggressive curettage and/or cold steel. With all visible gross tumor completely excised, an excision was made around the debulking defect. Hemostasis was obtained by spot electrodessication. A pressure dressing was placed. Tissue was divided into two tissue blocks which were mapped, color coded at their margins, and sent to the technician for frozen sectioning. Microscopic tumor was found persisting in none of the tissue blocks. Following surgery the defect measured as follows: 10 x 13 mm to the subcutaneous tissue. Closure will be by Burrow's graft.

Condition at termination of therapy: Carcinoma removed.

Pathology report on file.

What CPT® and ICD-9-CM codes are reported?

Case 3

Chief Complaint: The patient is a 42-year-old female with infected right axillary hidradenitis.

Procedure Note: With the patient in supine position and under general anesthesia, the right axilla was prepped and draped in the usual sterile fashion. A skin incision was made in the axilla to excise most of the hidradenitis tracts. The incision was carried down through the subcutaneous tissue. The underlying subcutaneous tissue was excised. Bleeding points were controlled by means of electrocautery. The subcutaneous tissues were closed in intermediate layers with a suture of 2-0 Vicryl. The skin edges were stapled together and a dry sterile dressing was applied. The patient tolerated the procedure well.

What are the CPT® and ICD-9-CM codes reported?

Case 4

Preoperative diagnosis: Segmental obesity of posterior thighs.

Postoperative diagnosis: Segmental obesity of posterior thighs.

Operative procedure: Posterior thigh lift with suction-assisted lipectomy of posterior medial thigh, bilateral.

Clinical note:

This obese patient presents for the above procedure. She understood the potential risks and complications including, but not limited to, the risk of anesthesia, bleeding, infection, wound healing problems, unfavorable scarring, and potential need for secondary surgery. She understood and desired to proceed.

Procedure:

The patient was placed on the operating table in supine position. General anesthesia was induced. She was positioned prone. The buttocks and thigh regions were prepped and draped in the usual sterile fashion. She had been marked in the awake, standing position, outlining the area for the incision along the gluteal crease that was in continuity with her medial thigh lift scar and extended to the posterior axillary line. The posterior medial thigh region was infiltrated with tumescent solution utilizing 750 mL. The liposuction was then accomplished, removing a total of 200 mL. The right side was addressed first. Then an incision was made along the gluteal crease at the desired site for the final incision. A posterior skin flap was elevated approximately 3 to 4 cm. Hemostasis was assured by electrocautery.

There was no residual flap or dead space and the fascia was closed at the deep level with 0 PDS and then in layers anatomically the closure was completed with 2-0, 3-0, and 4-0 PDS. Dermabond and Steri-Strips were applied. The medial third was also closed with a running 4-0 plain gut. The same was then accomplished on the left side in similar fashion and steps, achieving a symmetric result, and closure was accomplished similarly. A compression garment was applied. The patient was awakened, extubated, and transferred to the recovery room in satisfactory condition. There were no operative or anesthetic complications.

What are the CPT® and ICD-9-CM codes reported?

Case 5

Preoperative diagnosis: Panniculus, Diastasis recti.

Postoperative diagnosis: Panniculus, Diastasis recti.

Procedure performed: Abdominoplasty.

Anesthesia: General.

Clinical note: The patient has had multiple pregnancies, with diastasis recti occurring with the last pregnancy and for the above procedure. She understood the potential risks and complications including but not limited to the risks of anesthesia, bleeding, infection, wound healing problems, unfavorable scaring, and potential need for secondary surgery, and she desired to proceed. She also understood the possibility of impaired circulation to the flaps and hematoma/seroma formation.

Procedure in detail: The patient was placed on the operating table in supine position. General anesthesia was induced. The abdomen was prepped and draped in the usual sterile fashion and marked for abdominoplasty along the suprapubic natural skin crease. This coursed 36 cm in total. The umbilicus was also marked and the area was infiltrated with 100 cc of 0.5% Xylocaine with 1:200,000 epinephrine. After adrenaline effect, the incision was made. The flap was elevated to the umbilicus. The umbilicus was circum-scribed and dissected free, with care taken to maintain a generous vascular stalk. Dissec-tion was then taken to the subcostal margin as it tapered superiorly and narrowed the exposure. Hemostasis was obtained by electrocautery. There was still a lot of skin laxity and it appeared that the ellipse of skin could be removed through the superior margin of the umbilicus. The flap was incised at the midline for greater exposure.

She had significant diastasis recti, which was then closed with interrupted mattress sutures of 0 Ethibond, followed by a running suture of 0 Ethibond. She was placed in semi-flexed position and the ellipse of skin was excised to the superior margin of the umbilicus in the midline. This gave an easy fit for the flap without undue tension. The #15 drains were placed through the mons area and secured with 3-0 Prolene. The skin was then closed at Scarpa fascia with sutures of 2-0 PDS. The umbilicus site was marked and a disc of skin was removed. The umbilicus was delivered and sutured with dermal sutures of 4-0 PDS and the skin with 5-0 fast absorbing plain gut. Deep dermal repair was completed with reabsorbable staples and the skin was closed with a subcuticular suture of 4-0 PDS. Steri-Strips were applied over Mastisol. An abdominal binder was placed.

The patient was awakened, extubated, and transferred to the recovery room in satisfactory condition. There were no operative or anesthetic complications. Estimated blood loss was less than 30 cc.

What are the CPT® and ICD-9-CM codes reported?

Case 6

Preoperative diagnosis: Hypoplasia of the breast.

Postoperative diagnosis: Hypoplasia of the breast.

Operative procedure: Bilateral augmentation mammoplasty.

Anesthesla: General.

Operative summary: The patient was brought to the operating room awake and placed in a supine position where general anesthesia was induced without any complications. The patient's chest was prepped and draped in the usual sterile fashion. The patient had previous inframammary crease incisions on both left and right sides. The extent of the dissection would be to the sternal border within two fingerbreadths of the clavicle and slightly beyond the anterior axillary line. The left breast was operated upon first. An incision was made in the inframammary crease going through skin, subcutaneous tissue, down to the muscle fascia. Dissection at the subglandular level was then performed until an adequate pocket was made according to the previous limits. After irrigation with normal saline and careful hemostasis, a Mentor Allergan silicone filled high profile textured implant was used and placed into the pocket. It was 300 cc. The skin was then closed using 4-0 Vicryl in an interrupted fashion for the deep subcutaneous tissue 4-0 Monocryl in an interrupted fashion was used for the superficial subcutaneous tissue and the skin was closed using 4-0 Monocryl in a subcuticular fashion. Antibiotic ointment and Tegaderm were applied. The right breast was operated in a very similar fashion. The implant was a 340 cc silicone gel high profile textured implant from Allergan. Skin closure was the same. Both left and right breasts were very similar in size and shape. The patient had a bra applied. The patient tolerated this procedure well and left the operating room in stable condition.

What are the CPT® and ICD-9-CM codes reported?

Case 7

Preoperative diagnoses: Dysplastic nevus, right chest.

Postoperative diagnoses: Dysplastic nevus, right chest.

Procedures performed:
Excision, dysplastic nevus, right chest with excised diameter of 1.2 cm and complex repair of 3 cm wound.

Anesthesia: Local using 20 cc of 1% lidocaine with epinephrine.

Complications: None.

Estimated blood loss: Less than 2 cc.

Specimens:
Dysplastic nevus, right chest sutured at superior tip, 12 o'clock for permanent pathology.

Indications for surgery: The patient is a 49-year-old white woman with a dysplastic nevus of her right chest, which I marked for elliptical excision in the relaxed skin tension lines of her chest with gross normal margins of around 0.3 cm and I drew my best guess at the resultant scar and she observed these markings well and we proceeded.

Description of procedure: We started with the patient prone. The area has been infiltrated with local anesthetic. The chest prepped and draped in sterile fashion. I excised the dysplastic nevus as drawn into the subcutaneous fat. Hemostasis achieved using the Bovie cautery. Defects were created at each of the wounds to optimize the primary repair. Thus, I considered a complex repair and the wound is closed in layers using 4-0 Monocryl and 5-0 Prolene. A loupe magnification was used. The patient tolerated the procedure well.

Addendum: Pathology report confirms it is benign.

What are the CPT® and ICD-9-CM codes reported?

Case 8

Preoperative diagnoses:

1. Basal cell carcinoma right temple.
2. Squamous cell carcinoma, left hand.

Postoperative diagnoses: Same

Procedures performed:

1. Excision basal cell carcinoma right temple with excised diameter of 2.2 cm and full thickness skin graft 4 cm^2.
2. Excision squamous cell carcinoma, left hand with rhomboid flap repair 2.5 cm^2.

Anesthesia: Local using 8 cc of 1% lidocaine with epinephrine and 3 cc of 1% plain lidocaine.

Indications for surgery: The patient is a 77-year-old white woman with a biopsy-proven basal cell carcinoma of right temple that appeared to be recurrent and a biopsy-proven squamous cell carcinoma of her left hand. I marked the lesion of her temple for elliptical excision in the relaxed skin tension lines of her face with gross normal margins of around 2–3 mm and I marked my planned rhomboidal excision of the squamous cell carcinoma of her left hand with gross normal margins of around 3 mm and I drew my planned rhomboid flap. She observed all these markings with a mirror so she could understand the surgery and agree on the locations and we proceeded.

Description of procedure: All areas were infiltrated with local anesthetic, that is the anesthetic with epinephrine. The face and left upper extremity were prepped, draped in sterile fashion. I excised the lesion of her right temple and left hand as drawn to the subcutaneous fat. Hemostasis achieved with Bovie cautery. It took a few more passes to get the margins clear from the basal cell carcinoma right temple. The wound had become very large by that time around quarter sized and I attempted to close the wound. I began with a 3-0 Monocryl. It was simply too tight and was deforming her eyelid. Thus I felt that we would have to close with a skin graft. I marked the area of her right clavicle for the donor site and this area prepped and draped in a sterile fashion. I infiltrated with a plain lidocaine. The full-thickness skin graft harvested and defatted using scissors. Meticulous hemostasis achieved in the donor site using the Bovie cautery. The skin graft inset into the temple wound using 5-0 plain gut suture. The skin graft was vented and then a Xeroform bolster was placed using Xeroform and nylon. The donor site was closed in layers using 4-0 Monocryl and 5-0 Prolene. My attention turned to the hand. The margins had been cleared from that region even though it did take 2 passes. I incised the rhomboid flap and elevated with a full-thickness subcutaneous fat. Hemostasis achieved in the wound and the donor site using Bovie cautery. The flap rotated in the defect. The donor site closed with flap inset in layers using 4-0 Monocryl and 5-0 Prolene. Loupe magnification was used. The patient tolerated the procedure well.

What are the CPT® and ICD-9-CM codes reported?

Case 9

Preoperative diagnosis: Right breast mass.

Postoperative diagnosis: Right breast mass.

Procedure: Right breast lumpectomy.

Anesthesia: A 1% lidocaine with epinephrine mixed 1:1 with 0.5% Marcaine along with IV sedation.

Indications: The patient is a 23-year-old female who recently noted right breast mass. This has grown somewhat in size and we decided it should be excised.

Findings at the time of operation: This appeared to be a fibroadenoma.

Operative procedure: The patient was first identified in the holding area and the surgical site was reconfirmed and marked. Informed consent was obtained. She was then brought back to the operating room where she was placed on the operating room table in supine position. Both arms were placed comfortably out at approximately 85 degrees. All pressure points were well padded. A time-out was performed.

The right breast was prepped and draped in the usual fashion. I anesthetized the area in question with the mixture noted above. This mass was at the areolar border at approximately the outer central to upper outer quadrant. I therefore made a circumareolar incision on the outer aspect of the areola. This was carried down through skin, subcutaneous tissue and a small amount of breast tissue. I was able to easily dissect down to the mass itself. Once I was there, I placed a figure-of-eight 2-0 silk suture for traction. I then carefully dissected this mass out from the surrounding tissue. Once it was removed from the field, the traction suture was removed and the mass was sent in formalin to pathology. The wound was then inspected for hemostasis, which was achieved with electrocautery. I then reapproximated the breast tissue deep with interrupted 3-0 Vicryl suture and then another 3-0 Vicryl suture in the superficial breast tissue. The skin was then closed in a layered fashion using interrupted 4-0 Monocryl deep dermal sutures followed by a running 4-0 Monocryl subcuticular suture. Benzoin, Steri-Strips and a dry sterile pressure were then applied. The patient tolerated the procedure well and was taken back to the short stay area in good condition.

What are the CPT® and ICD-9-CM codes reported?

Case 10

Preoperative diagnosis: Necrotizing fasciitis.

Postoperative diagnosis: Necrotizing fasciitis.

Procedure: Wound excision and homograft placement with surgical preparation, exploration of distal extremity.

Findings and indications: This very unfortunate gentleman with liver failure, renal failure, pulmonary failure, and overwhelming sepsis was found to have necrotizing fasciitis last week. We excised the necrotizing wound. The wound appears to have stabilized; however, the patient continues to be very sick. On return to the operating room, he appears to have no evidence of significant healing of any areas with extensively exposed tibia, fibula, Achilles tendon, and other tendons in the foot as well as the tibial plateau and fibular head without any hope of reconstruction of the lower extremity or coverage thereof.

There was an area on the lateral thigh that we thought may be able to be closed with a skin graft eventually for a viable above-the-knee amputation.

Procedure in detail: After informed consent, the patient was brought to the operating room and placed in supine position on the operating table. The above findings were noted. Debridement sharply with the curved Mayo scissors and the scalpel were helpful in demonstrating the findings noted above. Because of the unviability of this area, it was felt that we would not perform a homografting to this area. However, the lateral thigh appeared to be viable and this was excised further with curved Mayo scissors. Hemostasis was achieved without significant difficulty and the homograft meshed 1.5:1 was then placed over the hemostatic wound on the lateral thigh. This was secured in place with skin staples.

Upon completion of the homografting, photos were also taken to demonstrate the rather desperate nature of this wound and the fact that it would require above-the-knee amputation for closure.

The wound was then dressed with moist dressing with incorporated catheters. The patient was taken back to the ICU in satisfactory condition.

What are the CPT® and ICD-9-CM codes reported?

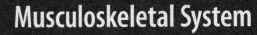
Case 1

Operative Report

Preoperative diagnosis: Comminuted left proximal humerus fracture

Postoperative diagnosis: Comminuted left proximal humerus fracture

Operative procedure: Open treatment of left proximal humerus.

Anesthesia: General.

Implants: DePuy Global fracture stem size 10 with a 48 x 15 humeral head.

Indications: The patient is a 66-year-old female who sustained a severely comminuted proximal humerus fracture. The risk and benefits of the surgical procedure were discussed. She stated understanding and desired to proceed.

Description of procedure: On the day of the procedure after obtaining informed consent, the patient was taken to the main operating room where she was prepped and draped in the usual sterile fashion in beach chair position after administering general anesthesia. Standard deltopectoral approach was used; the cephalic vein was taken laterally with the deltoid. Dissection carried out down to the fracture site. The fracture site was identified. The fragments were mobilized and the humeral head fragments removed. Once this was done, the stem was prepared up to a size 10. A trial reduction was carried out with the DePuy trial stem and implant head. This gave good range of motion with good stability. Sutures were placed in key positions for closure of the tuberosities down to the shaft including sutures through the shaft. The shaft was then prepared and cement was injected into the shaft. The implant was placed. Once the cement was hardened, the head was placed on Morse taper and then reduced. A bone graft was placed around the area where the tuberosities were being brought down. The tuberosities were then tied down with a suture previously positioned. This gave excellent closure and coverage of the significant motion at the repair sites. The wound was thoroughly irrigated. The skin was closed with Vicryl over a drain and also staples in the epidermis. A sterile dressing and sling was applied. The patient was taken to recovery in stable condition. No immediate complications.

What are the CPT® and ICD-9-CM codes reported?

Case 2

Preoperative diagnosis: Painful L2 vertebral compression fracture.

Postoperative diagnosis: Painful L2 vertebral compression fracture.

Name of operation: L2 kyphoplasty.

Findings preoperatively:
She had compression fractures at T 11 and L1, which underwent kyphoplasty and she initially had very good results, but then developed back pain once again. Repeat MRI a couple of weeks later showed that she had fresh high intensity signal changes in the body of L2 and some scalping of the superior end plate consistent with a compression fracture at L2. After some preoperative discussion and some patience to see if she would get better, she was admitted to the hospital for L2 kyphoplasty when she was not getting better. At surgery, L2 had some scalloping of the superior end plate. Most of the softness was in the back part of the vertebral body.

Procedure:
The patient was taken to the operating room and placed under general endotracheal anesthesia in a supine position. She was placed prone on the Jackson table and her back was prepped and draped in the usual sterile fashion. Using biplane image intensifiers, the skin incision sites were marked out. 0.5 Marcaine with epinephrine was injected. Initially on the left side, a Xyphon trocar was passed down to the superior lateral edge of the pedicle and then passed down through the pedicle and into the vertebral body—uneventfully in the usual fashion. The drill was then placed into the vertebral body and then the Kyphon bone tamp. In a similar fashion, the same thing was done on the other side. Balloons were then inflated uneventfully. The balloons were then deflated and removed and the cement when it was in the doughy state was then injected into the 2 sides in the usual fashion. This was done carefully and sequentially to make sure that there were no cement extrusions and in fact there were none, there was a good fill to the edges of vertebral body up towards the superior end plate and across the midline. The bone filling devices were then removed and the trocars removed. Pressure was applied after which the skin was sutured with 4-0 nylon. Band-Aids were applied and she was taken to recovery in stable condition.

Complications: There were no complications.

Blood loss: Minimal blood loss.

Counts: Sponge and needle counts were correct.

What are the CPT® and ICD-9-CM codes reported?

Case 3

Preoperative diagnosis: Comminuted intraarticular distal radial Colles' fracture left wrist.

Postoperative diagnosis: Comminuted intraarticular distal radial Colles' fracture left wrist.

Procedure: Application uniplane external fixation and closed reduction of left distal radial fracture under fluoroscopy.

Anesthesia: General endotracheal.

Description of the procedure:

After induction of adequate general endotracheal anesthesia, the patient's left upper extremity was routinely prepped and draped into a sterile field. The extremity was elevated and exsanguinated with an Esmarch bandage. The tourniquet was inflated to 300 millimeters of mercury. We first placed two half pins distally over the dorsoradial aspect of the second metacarpal first placing first pin in freehand technique making an incision, spreading with hemostat, and then placing the half pin. The second pin was placed identically by using the pin guide. Similarly, we placed pins in the dorsoradial aspect of the distal third of the radius. We then connected these 2 pins with clamps and then under C-arm control we reduced the fracture. All pins are now attached to the external fixation. This fracture at both dorsal and volar comminution and intraarticular fractures and was significantly shortened and telescoped. We obtained the best reduction possible and then tightened down the clamps to the bars. The pin tracks were dressed with Xeroform and 2 x 2 gauze and volar 3 x 15 plaster splints were applied. The tourniquet was allowed to deflate during application of the dressing. Total tourniquet time was 14 minutes. There were no intraoperative complications.

What are the CPT® and ICD-9-CM codes reported?

Case 4

Operative report

Preoperative diagnosis: Dislocation of right elbow.

Postoperative diagnosis: Dislocation of right elbow with medial epicondyle fracture.

Operative procedure: Closed reduction of elbow dislocation with a closed reduction of medial epicondyle fracture.

Anesthesia: General.

Indications: This is a 12-year-old male who sustained a dislocation of his right elbow. The risks and benefits of surgical treatment were discussed with the family who stated understanding and desired to proceed.

Description of procedure: On the day of procedure after obtaining informed consent, the patient was taken to the main Operating Room where general anesthia was induced. Once he was under adequate anesthesia the reduction maneuver was performed. The elbow was reduced and was stable. Through a full range of motion there was noted to be a slight crepitus on the medial elbow and it was felt some mobility in the medial epicondyle. Examination under C-arm imagery revealed a concentric reduction of the elbow but with mildly unstable medial epicondyle. When the elbow was held in the appropriate position the medial epicondyle was well reduced in acceptable position and it was elevated to treat this non-surgically and therefore a long arm splint was applied. The patient was awakened from anesthesia and taken to Recovery in stable condition with no immediate complications.

What are the CPT® and ICD-9-CM codes reported?

Case 5

Preoperative diagnosis: Right long finger trigger finger
                      Left shoulder impingement/subacromial bursitis.

Postoperative diagnosis: Right long finger trigger finger.
                       Left shoulder impingement/subacromial bursitis.

Procedures: Right long finger trigger release.
             Injection of the left shoulder with Xylocaine, Marcaine, and
             Celestone via anterior subacromial approach.

Anesthesia: General.

Complications: None.

Estimated blood loss: Minimal.

Replacement: Crystalloids.

Descripton of procedure: The patient was taken to the operating room where he was given appropriate anesthesia. The right upper extremity was prepped and draped in the usual sterile fashion. While the draping was going on, the left shoulder was prepped with Betadine and using Xylocaine. Marcaine and Celestone, through an anterior subacromial approach; the left shoulder was injected with 1 cc of Xylocaine, 1 cc of Celestone and 1 cc of Marcaine. The patient tolerated the procedure well.

Meanwhile, the right hand had been prepped and draped. It was exsanguinated with Esmarch and tourniquet inflated to 250 millimeters of mercury. I made an incision over the A1 pulley in the distal transverse palmar crease, about an inch in length. This was taken through skin and subcutaneous tissue. The Al pulley was identified and released in its entirety. Care was taken to avoid injury to the neurovascular bundle. The wound was irrigated with antibiotic saline solution. The subcutaneous tissue was injected with Marcaine without epinephrine. The skin was closed with 4-0 Ethilon suture. Clean dressing was applied. The patient was awakened and taken to the recovery room in stable condition.

What are the CPT® and ICD-9-CM codes reported?

Case 6

Preoperative diagnosis: Painful hardware left foot.

Postoperative diagnosis: Painful hardware left foot.

Procedure performed: Removal of hardware, left foot

Anesthesia: Sedation and local

Drain: None.

Estimated blood loss: Minimal.

Indications for procedure:
The patient had the above-mentioned problems, unresponsive to conservative treatment. We discussed the above-mentioned surgery, along with the potential risks and complications, and the patient understood and wished to proceed.

Description of procedure:
With the patient supine on the operating table after the successful induction of anesthesia, the left foot was prepped and draped in the usual sterile fashion, and then I injected 0.5% Marcaine into the area of the screw heads, both on the lateral side of the foot and then dorsal midfoot, about 5 mL each area. A small incision through the skin 0.5 cm, and blunt dissection down to the screw head. The screw was removed with the screwdrivers. They were irrigated and closed with simple 4-0 nylon sutures. A sterile compression dressing was applied. The patient was taken to the recovery room in satisfactory condition.

Material sent to laboratory: None.

Complications: None.

Condition on discharge: Satisfactory.

Discharge diagnosis: Painful hardware, left foot.

Discharge plan:
Discharge instructions were discussed with the patient. A copy of the instructions was given to the patient and a copy retained for the medical record. The following items were discussed: diet, activity, wound care medications if applicable, when to call the physician, and follow-up care.

What are the CPT® and ICD-9-CM codes reported?

Case 7

Procedure performed in office.

Preoperative diagnosis: Right-sided thoracic pain.

Postoperative diagnosis: Right-sided thoracic pain.

Operation: Trigger point injection into the right-sided thoracic spine musculature, into the rhomboid major, rhomboid minor, and levator scapular muscles.

Procedure:
The patient was seated on the bed. He was explained the risks, including but not limited to bleeding, infection, nerve damage and no guarantee of symptom relief. The patient has metastatic lung cancer and has had a right lung resection. The patient agreed and the informed consent was signed.

I palpated for areas of maximal tenderness. Five spots were marked into the right-sided thoracic paraspinal musculature. I then cleaned off his back with chlorhexidine x2. Then a 25 gauge 1.5 inch needle on a 10 cc controlled syringe with Depo-Medrol, 40 mg/mL was used. After negative aspiration, 1 cc was injected into each point. A total of four points were injected. A total of 4 cc (160 mg) was used. The patient tolerated the procedure well. Band-Aids were not placed. The patient was not bleeding.

We are also going to refill the patient's pain medication. He is seeing an oncologist and is getting Percocet 7.5/500. He takes four a day. That does provide him with pain relief. We are going to dispense to him today a three week supply. We are going to dispense #84. He is to return to the office in two weeks at which time we will get a urine for follow-up. Emphasized to the patient once again that he had to bring his pills to every appointment according to the opioid contract.

What are the CPT® and ICD-9-CM codes reported?

724.1

326   50

Case 8

Operative report

Preoperative diagnosis: Plantar fasciitis left.

Postoperative diagnosis: Same as preoperative diagnosis.

Procedures: Plantar fasciotomy left heel.

For informed consent, the more common risks, benefits, and alternatives to the procedure were thoroughly discussed with the patient. An appropriate consent form was signed, indicating the patient understands the procedure and its possible complications.

This 61-year-old male was brought to the operating room and placed on the surgical table in a supine position. Following anesthesia, surgical site was prepped and draped in the normal sterile fashion. Attention was then directed to the left heel where, utilizing a 61 blade, a stab incision was made, taking care to identify and retract all vital structures. The incision was deepened to the medial band insertion of the fascia. The fascia was then incised and avulsed from the calcaneus. The surgical site was then flushed with saline. 1 cc of Depo-Medrol was injected in the op site. Site was dressed with a light compressive dressing. Excellent capillary refill to all the digits was observed without excessive bleeding noted.

Hemostasis: none

Estimated blood loss: minimal

Injectables: Agent used for local anesthesia was 5.0 cc and Marcaine 0.5% with epi

Pathology: No specimen sent.

Dressings: Applied Bacitracin ointment. Site was dressed with a light compressive dressing.

Condition: Patient tolerated procedure and anesthesia well. Vital signs stable. Vascular status intact to all digits. Patient recovered in the operating room.

What are the CPT® and ICD-9-CM codes reported?

Case 9

Anesthesia: General anesthesia

Preoperative diagnosis: Left Achilles' tendon rupture.

Postoperative diagnosis: Left Achilles' tendon rupture.

Operation performed: Open Left Achilles' tendon repair.

Indications: The patient is 25-year-old male who was playing basketball when he was hit by another player and felt a pop in the back of his ankle approximately two months ago. Examination reveals a positive Thompson test, but no plantar-flexion on squeezing the calf. There is a palpable defect in the Achilles' tendon. There is some swelling in this region and neurovascular examination is intact. Given these clinical findings the patient is taken to the operating room for the aforementioned procedure.

Description of procedure: Following induction of general anesthesia the patient was placed prone on the operating table and all bony prominences were well-padded. The patient received a dose of one gram of Ancef. Under tourniquet control of 250 mm Hg, a longitudinal incision was made followed by an opening up the paratenon of the Achilles' tendon. An obvious rupture was noted. The hematoma was evacuated and the ends were then debrided with a Metzenbaum scissors. Using a #2 FiberWire® this was placed in a Bunnell type fashion in both the proximal and distal portions of the Achilles' tendon. Another #2 Orthocord was then used and placed in a running fashion along the proximal and distal portions of the Achilles' tendon. A total of four sutures were used. These were then tied together to re-approximate the tendon with no significant tension on the repair.

A nice secure repair was noted. The ends of the repair were also further augmented with a 2-0 Vicryl suture. The wound was thoroughly irrigated with antibiotics irrigation solution. The fascial plane was closed with a 2-0 Vicryl suture followed by closing the skin with a 2-0 in subcuticular fashion. Approximately 10 cc of 0.5% Marcaine was injected for postoperative pain control. A routine dressing was applied to the extremity and it was then placed into a short leg cast with the foot slightly plantar-flexed. In addition, the anterior aspect of the cast was then univalved. The tourniquet was deflated for a total tourniquet time of 42 minutes.

The patient was then awakened in the operating room breathing spontaneously and taken to the recovery room in stable condition.

What are the CPT® and ICD-9-CM codes reported?

27650

Case 10

Preoperative diagnosis: Right ankle triplane fracture

Postoperative diagnosis: Right ankle triplane fracture

Procedure: Open reduction and internal fixation (ORIF) right ankle triplane fracture

Anesthesia: General endotracheal

Complications: None

Specimen: None

Implant used: Synthes 4.0 mm cannulated screws

Indications for procedure:
The patient is a pleasant 15-year-old male who fell and sustained a right ankle triplane fracture. This was confirmed on both X-ray and CT scan. Explained to the patient are indications for ORIF as well as possible risks and complications which include but are not limited to infection, bleeding, stiffness, hardware pain, need for hardware removal, no guarantee of functional ambulatory result. The patient and the family understood and wished to proceed.

Procedure in detail:
The patient was brought back to operating room and placed on an operating table, given a general anesthetic without any complications, given preoperative antibiotics per usual routine. He had right lower extremity prepped and draped in the usual sterile fashion with alcohol prep followed by routine Betadine prep.

Under X-ray guidance, a pointed reduction clamp was placed from the anterolateral corner of the distal tibia to the medial side and reduced the triplane fracture. It was confirmed on both AP and lateral X-ray images that the gap was reduced. The patient then had guidewires taken from the Synthes 4.0 mm cannulated screw set, placed one from medial along the epiphysis on the anterior half of the epiphysis and parallel to the joint to catch the lateral aspect of the epiphysis. Then one screw was placed above the physis from anterior to posterior to capture that spike. Once wires were in appropriate position, length was measured, partially threaded 4.0 mm cancellous screws were selected so that all threads were across the fracture site. Appropriate length screws were placed, confirmed by X-ray to be in good position. Fracture was anatomically reduced, and ankle joint was anatomic. The patient had wounds copiously irrigated out. Closure was done with interrupted horizontal mattress 3-0 nylon suture. The patient had sterile compressive dressing, was placed into a 3-sided posterior mold splint, was extubated and brought to recovery room in stable condition. There were no complications. There were no specimens. Sponge and needle counts were equal at the end of the case.

What are the CPT® and ICD-9-CM codes reported?

27848

824.7

Case 1

Preoperative diagnosis: Recurrent Pleural effusion, Stage IV lung cancer

Postoperative diagnosis: Recurrent Pleural effusion, Stage IV lung cancer

Procedure performed: Right video assisted thoracoscopy, lysis of adhesions, talc pleurodesis

Procedure: Patient was brought to the operating room and placed in supine position. IV sedation and general anesthesia were administered per the Anesthesia Department. A double-lumen endotracheal tube was placed per Anesthesia. Position was confirmed by bronchoscopy. The patient was placed in the decubitus position with the right side up. The chest was prepped in the standard fashion with ChloraPrep, sterile towels, sheets and drapes. We had excellent isolation of the lung. However, we had poor exposure because there were a number of fibrous adhesions, a few of which were actually very dense. We immediately evacuated approximately 700 ml of fluid. However, once we entered the chest we encountered a number of loculated areas. We did not break down the adhesions. We gained enough exposure to do a complete talc pleurodesis. After lysing of adhesions, we were confident that we had access to the entire thoracic cavity. Eight grams of talc were introduced into the right thoracic cavity and strategically placed under direct vision. The chest tubes were then placed. The wounds were closed in layers. The patient tolerated the well and was taken to the recovery room in stable condition.

What are the CPT® and ICD-9-CM codes reported?

Case 2

Preoperative diagnosis: Malignant neoplasm glottis

Postoperative diagnosis: Malignant neoplasm glottis

Procedure:

An incision is made low in the neck. The trachea is identified in the middle and an opening is created to allow for the new breathing passage; tracheostomy tube is inserted and secured with sutures. Patient tolerated procedure well and is sent to recovery without complications.

What are the CPT® and ICD-9-CM codes reported?

161.0

Case 3

Preoperative diagnosis: Pedestrian involved in an MVA, left pneumothorax

Postoperative diagnosis: Pedestrian involved in an MVA, left pneumothorax

Procedure: Bronchoscopy, Left VATS, wedge resection

Procedure: Patient was brought into the operating room and placed in supine position. IV sedation and general anesthesia was administered per the Anesthesia Department. A single lumen endotracheal tube was placed for bronchoscopy. Due to the nature of the trauma we were interested in ruling out a bronchial tear. The bronchoscope was introduced into the mouth and passed into the throat without difficulty. There was no evidence of sanguineous drainage or bronchial trauma noted to the left mainstem. There were copious amounts of secretions noted and removed without difficulty. The right mainstem was also cannulated and found to be free of any unexpected trauma. The bronchoscopy was terminated at that time.

A double lumen endotracheal tube was placed per anesthesia. Position was confirmed by bronchoscopy. The patient was placed in the decubitus position with the left side up. The chest was prepped in standard fashion with Betadine, sterile towels, sheets and drapes. A small incision is made between two ribs and a standard port placement was utilized to gain access to the thoracic cavity. An endoscope is inserted into the chest cavity. Initially we had excellent exposure with good isolation of the lung. We were able to identify a large bleb at the apex of the left lung that was likely to be the source of the chronic air leak. We removed the apex with thoracoscopic green load for therapeutic correction of the patient's pneumothorax. The wounds were closed in layers. Chest tubes were placed. The patient tolerated the procedure well and was taken to the recovery room.

What are the CPT® and ICD-9-CM codes reported?

32666

868.

681.7

Case 4

Preoperative diagnosis:

1. Chronic hyperplastic rhinosinusitis

2. Allergies

3. Status post prior polypectomy and sinus surgery

Postoperative diagnosis: Same.

Operative procedure:
Left sinusotomy (three or more sinuses) to include:

▶ Nasal and sinus endoscopy

▶ Endoscopic intranasal polypectomy

▶ Endoscopic total sinus ethmoidectomy

▶ Endoscopic sphenoidotomy

▶ Endoscopic nasal antral windows, middle meatus, and inferior meatus

▶ Endoscopic removal of left maxillary sinus contents

Right sinusotomy (three or more sinuses) to include:

▶ Nasal and sinus endoscopy

▶ Endoscopic intranasal polypectomy

▶ Endoscopic total sinus ethmoidectomy

▶ Endoscopic sphenoidotomy

▶ Endoscopic nasal antral windows, middle meatus, and inferior meatus

▶ Endoscopic removal of right maxillary sinus contents

Specimens sent to pathology:

1. Left ethmoid and sphenoid contents for routine and fungal cultures

2. Right maxillary contents for routine and fungal cultures

3. Left intranasal ethmoid, sphenoid, and maxillary specimens for pathology

4. Right ethmoid, sphenoid, maxillary, and right intranasal contents for pathology

Findings: Complete nasal obstruction by polyps with obscuring of all of the normal landmarks. The right middle turbinate was found and preserved. The residual bode of the left middle turbinate was found and preserved. There was thickened hyperplastic mucosa throughout the sinuses with some polyps in the sinuses and the majority of the sinus cavities were filled with glue-like mucopurulent debris. At the end of the case there were no visible polyps, the airway was clear and the debris had been removed.

Procedure: The patient was taken to the operating room, placed in the supine position, and general endotracheal anesthesia adequately obtained. A pharyngeal pack was placed. The nose was infiltrated with xylocaine with epinephrine and cottonoids soaked in 4%

cocaine were placed. The procedure was performed in a similar manner on the left and right sides. The cottonoids were removed.

The 30-degree wide-angle sinus telescope with endoscrub and the Stryker Hummer device were used to remove the polyps starting anteriorly and working posteriorly. This led to visualization of the middle turbinates.

The middle meati disease was removed. The area of the uncinate process and infundibulum was shaved away and forceps were used to remove portions of bone particle. Using blunt dissection, the agger nasi cells, ethmoid and sphenoid sinuses were entered and the contents removed with forceps and suction. The inferior turbinates were infractured, a mosquito clamp placed through the lateral nasal wall into the maxillary sinuses through the inferior meatus. That opening was opened with forward and backward biting forceps, sinus endoscopy was performed, and inspissated mucus and debris cleaned out of the sinuses.

In a similar manner the sinuses were opened from the middle meatus and the sinuses cleaned. In the above manner, the ethmoid, sphenoid, and maxillary sinuses were cleaned of debris and inspissated mucus suctioned from the frontal recesses.

The patient was then suctioned free of secretions, adequate hemostasis noted. Gelfilm was soaked, rolled, and placed in the middle meati). Telfa gauze was impregnated with Bacitracin, folded and placed in the nose. Vaseline gauze was placed between the folds of Telfa. The pharyngeal pack was removed. He was suctioned free of secretions, adequate hemostasis noted, and the procedure terminated. He tolerated it well and left the operating room in satisfactory condition.

What are the CPT® and ICD-9-CM codes to report?

Case 5

Preoperative diagnoses:

1. Sarcoid

2. New onset paratracheal adenopathy

Postoperative diagnoses:

1. Sarcoid

2. New onset paratracheal adenopathy

Procedure performed:

Mediastinotomy

Description of procedure:

The patient was brought into the OR and placed in supine position. IV sedation and general anesthesia was administered by the anesthesia department. The neck was prepped in standard fashion with betadine scrub, sterile towels and drapes. Standard linear incision was made over the trachea. We were able to dissect down to the pretracheal fascia without difficulty. The extensive adenopathy was immediately apparent just below the innominate artery on the right paratracheal side. One exceedingly large lymph node was identified and biopsied extensively. Hemostasis was obtained without difficulty. The region was impregnated with marcaine, lidocaine, epinepherine mixture. The specimen was sent to pathology. The wound was closed in layers. The skin was closed with subcu stitch and covered with Dermabond. The patient tolerated the procedure well and was taken to the recovery room in stable condition.

What are the CPT® and ICD-9-CM codes reported?

Case 6

Preoperative diagnosis:
Loculated left pleural effusion, chronic

Postoperative diagnosis:
Loculated left pleural effusion, chronic

Procedure performed:
Attempted, ultrasound guided thoracentesis

Description of procedure:
The patient was prepped and draped in the sitting position. Using ultrasound guidance and 1% lidocaine, the thoracic catheter was introduced into the pleural space where we encountered very thick fibrous type pleura. Catheter was advanced and we were unable to aspirate any fluid. The catheter was removed. Sterile dressings were applied. Chest X-ray will be obtained for followup. Patient tolerated the procedure well.

What are the CPT® and ICD-9-CM codes for this procedure?

32555

511.9

Case 7

Preoperative Diagnosis: Left vocal cord tumor.

Postoperative Diagnosis: Left vocal cord tumor.

Name of Procedure: Direct laryngoscopy with microscope, removal of tumor.

Anesthesia: General.

Complications: None.

Specimens: Left vocal cord tumor to Pathology.

Blood Loss: Less than 10 ml.

Technique: Patient was brought into the operative suite and comfortably positioned on the table. General endotracheal anesthesia was induced. The bed was turned 90 degrees in a clockwise fashion. The alveolar guard was placed over the upper alveolus to protect the teeth. Appropriate drapes were placed. The anterior laryngoscope was then inserted and direct laryngoscopy was performed with no abnormal findings other than the above-described tumor. The scope was suspended and using the operating microscope the anterior vocal cord tumor was removed. The mucous membrane posterior to the tumor was carefully incised and Reinke's space was entered. Careful dissection allowed elevation of the mucous membrane off the anterior vocal cord up to the commissure with what appeared to be complete excision of the tumor. Minimal bleeding was noted. The area was sprayed with Cetacaine spray. The scope was gently removed. The teeth were evaluated and found to be free of any injury. The drapes and instruments were removed. The patient was returned to the care of Anesthesia, allowed to awaken, extubated and transported in stable condition to the recovery room having tolerated the procedure well.

Findings: Patient is a pleasant 77-year-old white female with a history of the above-noted diagnoses. Operative findings included an otherwise normal larynx with the exception of the left anterior vocal cord tumor. It was fairly soft.

What CPT® and ICD-9-CM codes should be used for this procedure?

Case 8

Preoperative diagnosis:

1. Mass, right upper lobe

Postoperative diagnosis:

1. Carcinoma, right upper lobe

Procedure performed:
VATS Right superior lobectomy

Description of procedure:
Under general anesthesia, after double-lumen tube intubation, the right lung was
collapsed and the right side up is oriented so the patient is in the left lateral decubitus
position. We prepped and draped the patient in the usual manner and gave antibiotics.
Then two 1 cm incisions were made along the posterior and mid axillary line at the ninth
and seventh intercostal spaces. The lung was deflated. A camera was inserted. A longer
(6 cm) incision was made along the fourth intercostal space anteriorly. We then freed up
some adhesions at the top of the lung, both in the superior area away from the tumor
and in the anterior mediastinal area. The tumor seemed to be in the right upper lobe.
The dissection was started by ligating the superior pulmonary vein and its branches and
the upper lobe was freed up. The small fissure was incomplete and I proceeded with the
lobectomy. The pulmonary artery branches were then ligated. The bronchus was ligated
as well. The superior branches to the upper lobe was then ligated with Endo GIA. The
lobe was freed up and sent to pathology. The wound was then closed in layers. A chest
tube was placed to suction and patient was sent to recovery in stable condition. Pathology
confirmed carcinoma.

What are the procedure and diagnoses codes for this procedure?

Case 9

Preoperative diagnosis:

1. Grade 3 squamous cell carcinoma of penis with inguinal lymphatic metastasis

Postoperative diagnosis

1. Grade 3 squamous cell carcinoma of penis with inguinal lymphatic metastasis

Procedure performed:
Laparoscopic bilateral pelvic lymphadenectomy

Description of procedure:
The patient is placed in supine position with thigh abduction. A 1.5 cm incision was made 2 cm distally of the lower vertex of the femoral triangle. The second incision was made 2 cm proximally and 6 cm medially. Two 10 mm Hasson trocars were inserted in these incisions. The last trocar was placed 2 cm proximally and 6 cm laterally from the first port.

Radical endoscopic bilateral pelvic lymphadenectomy was performed. The main landmarks—adductor longus muscle medially, the sartorius muscle laterally and the inguinal ligament superiorly—were well visualized. The retrograde dissection using the harmonic scalpel was started distally near the vertex of the femoral triangle towards the fossa ovalis, where safena vein was identified, clipped, and divided, and towards the femoral artery laterally. After the procedure, one can identify the skeletonized femoral vessels and the empty femoral channel, showing that the lymphatic tissue in this region was completely resected.

The surgical specimen was removed through the first port incision. A suction drain was placed to prevent lymphocele, and were kept until the drainage reached 50 mL or less in 24 h. Patient tolerated procedure well and was transferred to recovery in stable condition.

What CPT® and ICD-9-CM codes are reported?

Case 10

Preoperative diagnosis: Carcinoma, right lung and bronchus intermedius

Procedure Performed: Bronchoscopy

Description of procedure:
Two liters of oxygen was supplied nasally. The right nostril was anesthetized with two applications of 4% lidocaine and two applications of lidocaine jelly. The posterior pharynx was anesthetized with two applications of Cetacaine spray. The Olympus PF fiberoptic bronchoscope was introduced into the patient's right nostril. The posterior pharynx and epiglottis and vocal cords were normal. The trachea and main carina were normal. The entire tracheobronchial tree was then visually examined and the major airways. No abnormalities were noted on the left side. There was, however, extrinsic compression of the posterior segment of the right upper lobe. There also appeared to be submucosal tumor involving the bronchus intermedius between the right upper lobe and right middle lobe. Multiple washings, brushings, and biopsies were taken from the right upper lobe bronchus and bronchus intermedius. The specimens were sent for cytology and routine pathology. The patient tolerated this without any complications.

The CPT® and ICD-9-CM codes to report are:

Case 1

Preoperative diagnosis: Severe two-vessel coronary artery disease and moderate aortic stenosis.

Postoperative diagnosis: Same

Operation: Triple-vessel coronary artery bypass grafting: Left internal mammary artery to the left anterior descending coronary artery, reverse saphenous vein to the first diagonal branch, and a ramus intermedius. Aortic valve replacement with a 23 mm bovine pericardial bioprosthesis.

Anesthesia: General

Indications: This is a 66-year-old white male who presented with unstable angina pectoris. He underwent coronary angiography and was found to have a 70% distal left main, an 80% proximal LAD, a 95% proximal ramus intermedius, and a 70% lesion in the proximal diagonal branch. The right coronary artery had no significant lesions. His aortic valve gradient was 40 mm Hg by cath and echo. Because of his presentation with new onset of angina pectoris and significant coronary artery disease, surgery was warranted.

Procedure: While monitoring the intra-arterial blood pressure and EKG, the patient was anesthetized without incident. The entire chest, abdomen, and both legs were prepared and draped into the usual sterile field. A median sternotomy was performed. The left internal mammary artery was dissected off the chest wall. Simultaneously, the greater saphenous vein was harvested from the left leg endoscopically using a small incision. This was then closed in layers with Vicryl and Dermabond. A sterile compressive dressing was applied.

The pericardium was opened and tacked up to form a cradle. After heparinization, the ascending aorta and the right atrial appendage were cannulated and connected to cardio-pulmonary bypass using a membrane oxygenator with an initial flow of 4.9 liters/min. Antegrade and retrograde cardioplegia catheters were inserted. On bypass, a left ventricular vent was placed through the right superior pulmonary vein. The coronaries were dissected out and found to be suitable for grafting although the circumflex branches were less than 1mm in diameter. The ramus intermedius was identified as well as the diagonal branch which was small. The heart was then arrested with cold enriched blood cardioplegia given antegrade after cross-clamping the ascending aorta. Once diastolic arrest was obtained, the heart was cooled with cold blood cardioplegia given initially antegrade and subsequently retrograde. Additional doses were given retrograde as well as down the vein graft. At the end, a hot shot was given. Systemic temperature was lowered to 32 degrees. Myocardial temperature was maintained around 20 degrees.

The ramus intermedius was opened first. This was found to be a 1.5-2.0 mm vessel. An end-to-end anastomosis using a segment of reverse saphenous vein was then performed with running 7-0 Prolene suture technique. This was felt to be a good graft with flow of 90 ml/min.

Next, the first diagonal branch was grafted in a similar manner with a second segment of reverse saphenous vein with a resultant flow of 50 ml/min.

The left internal mammary artery was anastomosed to the left anterior descending coronary artery in an end-to-end fashion using the in situ left mammary with running 8-0 Prolene suture technique. The diagonal branch was a 1.5 mm vessel and the LAD was a 1.5–2.0 mm vessel.

Next, the aorta was opened in an oblique transverse fashion and a moderately calcified trileaflet aortic valve was encountered. This was excised and the annulus debrided of a small amount of calcium. The left ventricle was irrigated with saline. The annulus sized to a 23 mm pericardial tissue valve (Model #3000, Serial # 55555555). The valve was sutured in; in a supra-annular fashion with interrupted 2-Ethibond valve sutures placed in the pledgets on the left ventricular out-flow tract side. The valve was seated and tied down securely. The aortotomy was then closed in two layers with running 4-0 Prolene reinforced within the corners pledgets.

During the same cross-clamp time, the proximal vein grafts were then anastomosed to the ascending aorta to two separate circular openings using 6-0 Prolene suture technique. After filling the heart with blood and evacuating the air from the apex of the left ventricle with an 18-gauge needle, the cross-clamp was removed and the vein graft de-aired. Rewarming had begun while constructing the proximal anastomoses. While rewarming continued, two temporary atrial, temporary ventricular, and temporary ground pacing wires were placed as well as two Blake drains for mediastinal drainage.

Once the patient reached a rectal temperature of 36 degrees, he was weaned off cardiopulmonary bypass without any inotropic support and without any difficulties. The venous cannula was removed; the heparin reversed with protamine, and the aortic cannula was removed. The mediastinum was irrigated with copious amounts of saline and Bacitracin solution using the pulse lavage irrigator.

The sternum was reapproximated with the surgical Pioneer Cable System using four figure-of-eight cables. After pulse irrigating, pulse lavaging and the fascia and subcutaneous tissue, the incision was closed in layers with Vicryl and the skin reapproximated with a subcuticular closure and Telfa sterile dressing was applied. There were no difficulties and the patient was taken to the ICU in stable condition.

What are the CPT® and ICD-9-CM codes reported?

Case 2

Preoperative diagnosis: Coronary artery disease. Hypercholesterolemia

Postoperative diagnosis: Same

Operation: Coronary artery bypass graft X 4. Left internal mammary artery to obtuse marginal artery, right internal mammary artery to the left anterior descending artery, reverse saphenous vein to the first diagonal artery and reverse saphenous vein graft to the right posterior descending artery.

Indications: The patient is a 39-year-old gentleman with a history of hypercholesterolemia, hypertension, and mild to moderate obesity, who presents with a positive stress test. Catheterization revealed the left main, circumflex disease as well as total right coronary artery disease.

Procedure: The patient was brought to the operating room and placed on the operating table in the supine position. After the induction of general endotracheal anesthesia, the patient was prepared and draped in the usual sterile fashion. We proceeded to harvest vein endoscopically from the left lower extremity. At the same time, the LIMA and then RIMA were harvested by open technique.

The patient was heparinized. The conduits were prepared for bypass. We proceeded to open the cardiac cradle, cannulated the ascending aorta and right atrium. Antegrade and retrograde cardioplegia catheters were placed. At this time, we placed the patient on cardiopulmonary bypass. The targets were examined and they seemed to be graftable. At this point, we proceeded to place a cross-clamp on the ascending aorta and arrested the heart with antegrade and retrograde cardioplegia, topical ice, and cooled down to 32C.

At this point, we exposed the territory of the RPDS. It was found to be a modest target. A reverse saphenous vein graft to right posterior descending artery graft was fashioned using 7-0 Prolene. Flow was measured at 50 ml/min. Next, we directed our attention to the first diagonal artery. It was also a modest target. It was opened. The anastomosis was fashioned using the reverse saphenous vein graft with 7-0 Prolene. Flow was measured at 60 ml/min. At this point, we exposed the territory of the obtuse marginal. The left internal mammary was prepared. The LIMA to obtuse marginal graft was performed with 7-0 Prolene. There was excellent hemostasis. We tacked down the wings of the mammary. The bull-dog was placed on the mammary.

At this point, we proceeded to perform two proximal aortotomies with the 4.0 mm aortic punch. Two proximal anastomoses were fashioned after the veins were cut to length with 6-0 Prolene. Bull-dogs were placed on each of these veins.

At this point, we proceeded to rewarm the patient. The territory of the left anterior descending artery was exposed. The RIMA was prepared. The RIMA to LAD anastomoses was fashioned using the 7-0 Prolene. Once this was completed, the wings of the mammary were tacked.

At this point, warm cardioplegia was given in retrograde fashion. The bull-dogs were removed from both the LIMA and the RIMA. We resumed perfusion of the heart. We proceeded to de-air the root of the aorta, and at this point proceeded to remove the cross-clamp. The patient resumed a normal sinus rhythm. The sites were oversewn; the vein grafts were de-aired in the usual fashion.

We examined the proximal and distal anastomoses and there was excellent hemostasis. Three Blake drains were placed, two into the mediastinum and one into the right pleura as we did not enter the left pleural space. The patient was weaned off cardiopulmonary bypass without any difficulty. The sternum was reapproximated with heavy stainless steel wire in a mattress fashion. The pectoralis fascia and subcutaneous tissue were approximated with 1-Vicryl skin with 4-0 Vicryl as well as Dermabond. The lower extremities were closed in similar fashion. The instrument counts were correct. The patient was transferred to the SICU in stable condition.

What are the CPT® and ICD-9-CM codes reported?

Case 3

Preoperative diagnoses: Critical aortic stenosis, coronary artery disease, hypertension, diabetes mellitus

Postoperative diagnoses: Same

Operation: Aortic valve replacement with a 19 mm St. Jude bioprosthesis. Coronary artery bypass graft x 2—reverse saphenous vein graft to left anterior descending artery and reverse saphenous vein graft to obtuse marginal artery.

Anesthesia: general

Indications: This is an 80-year-old female with a history of hypertension, diabetes mellitus, and coronary artery disease who presented to the emergency department with a syncopal episode. An echo revealed severe to critical aortic stenosis. Cath confirmed this diagnosis as well as two-vessel coronary artery disease with a tight proximal left anterior descending artery lesion as well as a tight circumflex lesion, and a 40% right coronary artery lesion.

Procedure: The patient was brought to the operating room and placed on the table in the supine position. After induction of general anesthesia, the patient was prepped and draped in the usual sterile fashion.

We proceeded to harvest the vein endoscopically from the left lower extremity. Once we were ready to divide the conduit, the patient was heparinized. The conduit was divided and prepared for bypass. A median sternotomy was performed, there was a pericardial cradle.

We cannulated the ascending aorta. Antegrade and retrograde cardioplegia catheters were placed. The patient was placed on cardiopulmonary bypass with an ACT greater than 400. We examined the targets and they were deemed to be graftable.

At this point, the pulmonary artery was dissected off the aorta. We placed a vent through the right superior pulmonary vein. At this point, we proceeded to cross-clamp the ascending aorta and gave cardioplegia in antegrade and retrograde fashion, as well as topical ice. We cooled the patient to 32 C.

With an excellent arrest, we exposed the territory of the obtuse marginal. It was opened, found to be a graftable vessel. A reverse saphenous vein graft to the obtuse marginal was fashioned using 7-0 Prolene. The flow was measured at 90 ml/min.

At this point, the territory of the LAD was exposed. It was opened, and a reverse saphenous vein graft to left anterior descending artery anastomosis was fashioned using 7-0 Prolene. Flow was measured at 110 ml/min. Cardioplegia was given down these grafts as well as in a retrograde fashion throughout the case, every 20 minutes.

At this point, we proceeded to perform a hockey-stick incision of the aorta approximately 1.5 cm above the right coronary artery. We proceeded to use silk sutures to expose the aortic valve. It was a severely calcified, trileaflet aortic valve. The leaflets were cut out. The annulus was debrided. We irrigated the ventricle, then we proceeded to size the valve to a 19 mm valve. Sutures of 2-0 Ethibond were placed in ventriculoaortic fashion circumferentially. They were then passed through the valve. The valve was seated and tied down without any difficulty. The right and left coronary ostia appeared to be intact and free of any obstruction. There appeared to be no evidence of weakness around the annulus.

We proceeded to rewarm the patient. The aorta was closed using two layers of 4-0 Prolene with two felt strips. We proceeded to perform two proximal aortotomies once the veins were cut to length. The veins had bull-dogs on them. At this point we proceeded to remove the cross-clamp and normal sinus rhythm was reinstituted.

Ventricular pacing wires were placed and after de-airing maneuvers, the vent was removed. We placed Blake drains into the mediastinum x 2.

What are the CPT® and ICD-9-CM codes reported?

Case 4

Preoperative diagnosis: Ischemic cardiomyopathy. Intraventricular conduction delay. Congestive heart failure.

Postoperative diagnosis: Same

Operation: Insertion of left ventricular epicardial pacemaker lead with generator change.

Indications: Ischemic cardiomyopathy with intraventricular conduction delay in a patient experiencing congestive heart failure, status post failed attempt at placement of transvenous coronary sinus lead.

Procedure: The patient was brought to the operating room and after having the appropriate monitoring devices placed was intubated and general endotracheal anesthesia was achieved. The patient was prepared and draped in the usual sterile fashion.

The chest was entered via a small left posterior thoracotomy. The left anterior chest generator pocket was opened and the generator explanted. The left lung was collapsed. The pericardium was opened and two unipolar epicardial leads were placed in the posterolateral left ventricle. Thresholds were checked and found to be adequate. The leads were tunneled subcutaneously to the generator pocket.

A new St. Jude biventricular pacing implantable cardioverter-defibrillator generator was then reconnected to the transvenous atrial and ventricular leads as well as to the epicardial lead. The generator was again interrogated and the thresholds and impedances of all leads were found to be adequate. The generator was replaced in the pocket. The pocket was irrigated with antibiotic saline and closed in layers with Vicryl suture.

A single left pleural drain was placed and a single pericostal suture was utilized to reapproximate the ribs. The fascia and subcutaneous tissue were closed with layered Vicryl suture and the skin was closed with a subcuticular stitch.

The patient was transferred to the Coronary Care Unit in stable condition having tolerated the procedure well.

What are the CPT® and ICD-9-CM codes reported?

Case 5

Preoperative diagnosis: Sinus of Valsalva aneurysm on the left coronary sinus

Postoperative diagnosis: Same

Operation: Repair sinus of valsalva aneurysm with pericardial patch

Procedure: The patient was taken to the operating room and placed supine on the table. After general endotracheal anesthesia was induced, rectal temperature probe, a Foley catheter and TEE probe were placed. The extremities were padded in the appropriate fashion. Her neck, chest, abdomen and legs were prepared and draped in standard surgical fashion.

The chest was opened through a standard median sternotomy. The patient was fully heparinized and placed on cardiopulmonary bypass. At this point we started to open the pericardium. We were met with a large amount of dense adhesions and some fluid that was blood-tinged, salmon colored and it was cultured. Tonsil clamps were placed on the inferior portion of the pericardial sac and we used Bovie cautery and Metzenbaum scissors to take down all the adhesions laterally, exposing the right atrium first and then the aorta. There were some lighter adhesions over the left ventricle, which were broken with finger dissection. There was a moderate amount of fluid in different pockets that were suctioned free. There was no evidence of any frank blood.

After dissecting out the right atrium, we dissected out the aorta circumferentially using Bovie cautery and Metzenbaum scissors. We then freed up the entire LV and the apex, as well as the inferior and lateral borders of the heart. After this we then checked the ACT which was greater than 550. The ascending aorta was cannulated without any difficulty. A dual stage venous cannula was placed in the right atrium. Retrograde cardioplegia was placed in the right atrium through the coronary sinus and antegrade cardioplegia was placed in the ascending aorta.

After the patient was on bypass, we completed dissection. We looked through the superior pulmonary vein. It appeared to be densely adhesed, so we opted to vent through the apex of the LV. We proceeded to flush our lines, cooled to 32 degrees. Once we had a nice arrest we opened the aorta. An aortotomy was created in standard fashion and the area was tacked back and we were able to identify the aneurysm in question. There was a large amount of thrombus and it was removed. There was also some mural thrombus which was laminar and stuck to the aneurysm and I elected not to debride this area.

This defect apparently took up the entire left of the sinus of Valsalva. The coronary was probed and there was approximately 2–3 mm rim of tissue beneath the coronary to sew to, and the valve was intact. The aortic valve was intact and there was a rim of tissue just lateral to the annulus for us to sew to. After debriding and irrigating, we then proceeded to size a bovine pericardial patch and sutured it in place with 4-0 Prolene suture. This was done in a running fashion, working from the annulus up towards the coronary artery underneath the coronary, and then around laterally and superiorly, sewing through the aortic tissue.

We now successfully excluded the aneurysm and packed the entire sinus. We gave cardioplegia in a retrograde fashion, with nice flow back from the left main. We inspected the repair and it was competent. We irrigated one more time and proceeded to close the aorta, de-aired the heart with standard maneuvers and removed the cross-clamp. We then weaned the patient off of bypass. There was no aortic insufficiency, good function of the aortic valve, no flow into the aneurysm anymore, with a nice patch repair. We then closed the chest with stainless steel wires, the fascia was closed with Vicryl sutures, and subcutaneous tissue and skin were closed in similar fashion.

What are the CPT® and ICD-9-CM codes reported?

Case 6

Preoperative Diagnosis: 6.7 cm descending thoracic aortic aneurysm. Type B aortic dissection, chronic.

Postoperative Diagnosis: Same

Operation: Left thoracotomy. Repair of a descending thoracic aortic aneurysm with a 34 mm Gelweave graft.

Bypass Time: 1 hour, 15 minutes

Procedure: The patient was brought to the operating room, placed on the table in the supine position. A blocker was placed on the left main stem bronchus and we isolated the left lung. We proceeded to place the patient in the right lateral decubitus position. He was padded and secured with all pressure points relieved and we proceeded at this point to prepare and drape the patient in the usual sterile fashion.

At this point we proceeded to perform a left posterolateral thoracotomy, dividing the muscles the fourth intercostal space was entered. The lung was completely deflated. At the same time we proceeded to expose the left common femoral vein as well as the left common femoral artery and at this point heparinized the patient. These vessels were isolated and prepared for cannulation.

A venous line was placed into the right atrium through the common femoral vein and this was secured. The patient was placed on partial bypass maintaining a blood pressure in the lower extremities of around 50 mm Hg. We continued at this point with our dissection. The esophagus was plastered against the aorta. It was peeled off. Intercostals were controlled and divided. At this point, we proceeded to place an aortic cross-clamp proximally and distally and we entered the aneurysm. We identified two lumens and these were resected and proximally we identified the true lumen and resected the false lumen after obtaining control of the subclavian artery. Distally we fenestrated the wall between the true and false lumen to prevent any malperfusion.

At this point, we proceeded to size the aorta to a 34 mm aortic graft and we proceeded to fashion the proximal anastomosis using 3-0 Prolene with a large needle in a running fashion. We proceeded to nerve hook this suture line and proceeded to tie this down. The posterior suture line of the proximal anastomosis was reinforced with 4-0 Prolene pledgeted stitches. At this point, we removed the cross-clamp and pressurized the anasto-moses. Areas of leak were controlled with 4-0 Prolene. At this point, the graft was cut to length and after examining our distal aorta and making sure an appropriate fenestration had been performed we proceeded to fashion an anastomosis again using 3-0 Prolene with a large needle. Before removing the proximal cross-clamp we proceeded to de-air the graft with a 25 gauge needle. We very slowly removed the proximal cross-clamp as well as the distal cross-clamp and flow was reinstituted down the aorta. We weaned the patient off bypass and examined our distal and proximal anastomoses. All incisions were closed and the patient tolerated the procedure well.

What are the CPT® and ICD-9-CM codes reported?

Case 7

Preoperative diagnosis: Prosthetic valve endocarditis

Postoperative diagnosis: Same

Operation: Re-replacement of 10–year-old tricuspid valve using a 31 mm Carpentier-Edwards pericardial bioprosthesis

Procedure: The patient was brought to the operating room and after having the appropriate monitoring devices placed, he was intubated and general endotracheal anesthesia was achieved. The patient was prepared and draped in the usual sterile fashion.

The chest was entered via a median sternotomy incision. Simultaneous to this, the right common femoral vein was dissected. The pericardium was opened, the patient was given systemic heparin, and the ascending aorta and superior vena cave were cannulated. Similarly, the right common femoral vein was cannulated. The patient was started on bypass.

Caval snares were placed, and the right atrium was opened. An intra-atrial thrombus excised and cultured. The prosthetic valve was excised and the annulus debrided, and any thrombus debrided and irrigated. The valve was sized and a 31 mm valve was selected.

Pledgeted 2-0 Ethibond sutures were passed circumferentially around the annulus in a ventriculoatrial fashion. These sutures were tied and the valve was inspected. The valve was found to be well-seated, and the atrium was closed with running 4-0 Prolene sutures.

The patient was rewarmed, de-aired, and then weaned from bypass with low-dose inotropic support. Temporary drains were placed and the mediastinum was policed for hemostasis and the sternum reapproximated with stainless steel wire. The femoral vein and groin wounds were closed with layered Vicryl sutures. The patient was taken back to the Cardiac Surgical Unit in stable condition after tolerating the procedure well.

What are the CPT® and ICD-9-CM codes reported?

Case 8

Preoperative diagnosis: Multiple varicose veins with severe pain in the leg.

Postoperative diagnosis: Same

Procedure: Removal of multiple varicose veins, right lower leg involving both the greater and lesser saphenous systems.

Anesthesia: General.

Procedure: With the patient prepped and draped in the usual sterile manner, multiple small incisions were made over the patient's varicose veins in the right leg. Through these incisions multiple clusters and branches from the greater saphenous vein and lesser saphenous veins were removed. Dilated tortuous segments of the greater saphenous vein and lesser saphenous vein were also removed. Most of the greater saphenous vein was removed. Meticulous hemostasis was achieved. All perforators associated with these clusters were ligated with 3-0 Vicryl suture. The patient's leg was wrapped in sterile Webril and Ace wrap. There were no complications.

What are the CPT® and ICD-9-CM codes reported?

Case 9

Preoperative diagnosis: Cardiac tamponade secondary to malignant effusion

Postoperative diagnosis: Same

Procedure: Pericardial window via subxiphoid approach

Details: The patient was positioned supine on the table and prepped and draped. A low midline incision approximately 5 cm in length was made over the sternum and xiphoid. This was carried down to the linea alba, which was opened. The xiphoid was divided. We then found the pericardium and opened the pericardium again with electrocautery. We enlarged the site so it was easily 1cm across. At this time there was a gush of fluid under pressure. It was serosanguinous fluid. It was not turbid, nor was there any odor. We suctioned this fluid for approximately 500 ml in the suction container. There was probably an additional 100 ml of spill on the drapes. Approximately 100 ml was also sent for cytology and culture.

After we felt we had fully drained the pericardium and had a significant hemodynamic improvement, we then made a small transverse incision to the right of her lower sternal incision and through this and across the fascia, we passed a #20-French Blake drain. This was placed on the diaphragmatic surface of the heart and was tied in place using 2-0 Ethibond sutures. We then closed the fascia with 0 Vicryl and the subcutaneous tissue with 0 Vicryl, these were all interrupted, and the skin with staples. At the end of the procedure the patient's condition remained stable.

What are the CPT® and ICD-9-CM codes reported?

Case 10

Preoperative diagnosis: Acute renal failure

Postoperative diagnosis: Same

Indication: Patient is a 23-year-old critically ill woman who went to the operating room for a lung transplant. A Vas-Cath was indicated to proceed with CVVHD upon arrival in the ICU.

Procedure: Left subclavian Vas-Catheter placement (insertion)

The left chest was draped and prepped in the usual sterile fashion and the patient was placed in the Trendelenburg position. The subclavian vein was readily located with a needle and the Seldinger technique was used to place a Vas-Cath for dialysis. Excellent flow was returned through both lumens. The catheter was secured in place and a sterile dressing applied. The patient is to be transported to the ICU where a postprocedural X-ray will be taken.

What are the CPT® and ICD-9-CM codes reported?

Case 1

Preoperative diagnosis: History of Rectal carcinoma

Postoperative diagnosis: History of Rectal carcinoma

Procedure performed: Closure of loop ileostomy with small bowel resection and entero-enterostomy with intraoperative flexible sigmoidoscopy.

Description of procedure: After induction of adequate general endotracheal anesthesia, the patient was carefully positioned in the supine modified lithotomy position in Allen stirrups. Great care was taken to carefully pad and protect all areas of potential bodily injury. Digital rectal examination revealed a widely patent circumferentially intact pouch anal anastomosis within 1 cm of the dentate line. Flexible sigmoidoscopy was performed revealing healthy pink mucosa. The abdomen was prepped and draped in the usual sterile manner and a parastomal incision was made and carried down sharply into the peritoneal cavity. Meticulous hemostasis was obtained with electrocautery. A 360 degree subfascial mobilization was undertaken until approximately 40 cm of each the afferent and efferent limb reached above the skin in a tension-free manner. Betadine was insufflated down each limb to verify that no enterotomies or seromyotomies were made. The mesentery was scored and vessels divided with a 10 mm LigaSure Impact. The bowel was circumferentially cleared of fat proximally and distally and each end divided with a GIA 100 mm stapling device with blue cartridge. The field was protected with blue towels and the antimesenteric border of each staple line was excised. A side-to-side functional end- to-end anastomosis was fashioned with a GIA 100 mm stapling device. The staple line was reinforced for hemostasis with 3-0 PDS 2 suture where necessary and the afferent limb was secured to the efferent limb with 3-0 PDS 2 seromuscular Lembert type sutures. After verification of the meticulous hemostasis, the apical enterotomy was secured with a GIA 100 mm stapling device. The anastomosis was healthy pink and widely patent and circumferentially intact and easily returned into the peritoneal cavity. After copious irrigation and verification of meticulous hemostasis.

What are the CPT® and ICD-9-CM codes reported?

 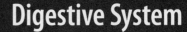

Case 2

Preoperative diagnosis: Right-sided colonic polyps

Postoperative diagnosis: Right-sided colonic polyps

Procedure: Laparoscopic right hemicolectomy with ileocolic anastomosis.

Procedure as follows: After induction of adequate general endotracheal anesthesia, the patient was carefully positioned in the supine modified-lithotomy position and Allen stirrups. Great care was taken to carefully pad and protect all areas of potential bodily injury. The abdomen was prepped and draped in the usual sterile manner.

Using a supra-umbilical vertical incision, a Hasson technique was employed to carefully place a 10 mm canula. Carbon dioxide pneumoperitoneum of 15 mm Hg was achieved, after which a 30-degree telescope was carefully introduced. Under direct vision, two left-sided ports were placed, one in the left lower quadrant, one in the left upper quadrant, each lateral to the epigastric vessels through horizontal stab wounds. With a combination of head up, head down, and right side up, the entire right colon was mobilized from the duodenum, pancreas, and right ureter, using 10 mm diameter Babcock grasping forceps and 5 mm diameter harmonic scalpel.

After complete mobilization and copious irrigation and verification of meticulous hemostasis, the supraumbilical port was lengthened to 4 cm, through which an Alexis wound protector was placed. The entire right colon was withdrawn. High ligation of the ileocolic arcade and the right branch of the middle colic were undertaken using 10 mm diameter LigaSure Atlas. The Atlas was used for the remaining mesentery. The bowel was circumferentially cleared of fat proximally and distally, and each end divided with a GIA 100 mm stapler with blue cartridge. The field was draped with blue towels, and the antimesenteric border of each staple line was excised along with the terminal ileum. A side-to-side, functional end-to-end anastomosis was fashioned with a GIA 100 mm stapling device with blue cartridge between the remaining ileum and colon. The staple line was verified for hemostasis, after which the afferent limb was secured to the efferent limb with 3-0 PDS II seromuscular Lembert-type sutures. After verification of anastomotic hemostasis, the apical enterotomy was secured with a GIA 100 mm stapling device with blue cartridge. The anastomosis was healthy, pink, widely patent, circumferentially intact, and easily returned into the peritoneal cavity.

After copious irrigation and verification of meticulous hemostasis, the fascia was closed with interrupted #1 Vicryl plus figure-of-eight sutures. The subcutaneous layers were irrigated and verification of meticulous hemostasis. Port sites were closed in a similar manner. The skin was closed, and covered by dry dressings, and the patient was discharged to the recovery room in stable condition, without having suffered any apparent operative complications.

What are the CPT® and ICD-9-CM codes reported?

Case 3

Procedure: Uvulopalatopharyngoplasty.

Indication: A 63-year-old with obstructive sleep apnea. He is intolerant of CPAP.

Procedure: I identified the patient and he was brought to the operating room. General endotracheal anesthesia was induced without complication. Tonsillar pillars and palate were injected with 0.25% Marcaine. The right tonsil was grasped with an Allis forceps and dissected from the tonsillar fossa with a combination of blunt and cautery dissection. The posterior pillar remained intact as I proceeded to do the similar mobilization of the left tonsil. I then made a mucosa incision across the base of the palate approximately 0.5 cm from the base of the uvula, connecting the anterior tonsillar incisions. Muscular portion of the uvula and edge of the soft palate was then opened. Posterior pillar was opened inferiorly on the right tonsil fossa, and extended through the palate to include the uvula, and then extended inferiorly on the left side. The uvula, edge of the soft palate, and both tonsils were removed en toto. Hemostasis was achieved with electrocautery. The mucosal incision was then closed with interrupted Vicryl sutures. The oral cavity was irrigated with Clindamycin solution.

The patient was returned to Anesthesia, extubated, and brought safely to the recovery room.

What are the CPT® and ICD-9-CM codes reported?

Case 4

Preoperative diagnosis: Morbid obesity. BMI 40.

Postoperative diagnosis: Morbid obesity. BMI 40.

Procedure performed: Laparoscopic sleeve gastrectomy. Intraoperative esophagogastroduodenoscopy. Intraoperative endoscopy.

Anesthesia: General endotracheal anesthesia.

Operative Procedure: The patient was brought to the operating room and placed on the OR table in supine position. Once general endotracheal anesthesia was achieved and preop antibiotics were given, the abdomen was prepped and draped in the standard surgical fashion. Access to the abdominal cavity was through a 1 cm supraumbilical incision with an Optiview trocar. CO_2 was insufflated to achieve an intraabdominal pressure of approximately 15 mm Hg. Accessory trocars were placed in the subxiphoid, right, mid and left upper quadrants of the abdomen, as well as in the right and left lower quadrants of the abdomen. All this was done under appropriate videoscopic observation.

The pyloric channel is then identified and approximately 4 cm proximal to it, the short gastric vessels of the greater curvature are taken down all the way up to the GE junction with the harmonic scalpel. A 38 French bougie is passed into the stomach into the pyloric channel and with the help of the linear cutter; the stomach is transected in a vertical fashion creating a gastric tube which is approximately 100 mL in diameter. The staple line is then oversewn with a running 2-0 Vicryl suture. Good hemostasis was achieved.

Then I proceeded to perform intraoperative esophagogastroduodenoscopy. The scope was advanced through the oropharynx and under direct vision it was taken down through the esophagus and into the sleeve. There was no evidence of leak, bleeding, or any other abnormalities. A patent sleeve was seen all the way down to the pylorus. The scope was then retrieved carefully.

A placement of a drain through the subhepatic space and extraction of the specimen through a right lower quadrant incision was done. All trocars were removed under appropriate videoscopic observation. There was no evidence of bleeding from any of the trocar sites. All the trocar sites were sutured closed and injected with local anesthesia. The patient tolerated the procedure well. He was extubated on the table and transferred to the recovery room in stable condition. There were no complications.

What are the CPT® and ICD-9-CM codes reported?

Case 5

Preoperative diagnosis: Cholelithiasis, Chronic Cholecystitis and acute pancreatitis

Postoperative diagnosis: Cholelithiasis, Chronic Cholecystitis and acute pancreatitis, pathology pending

Procedure performed: Laparoscopic cholecystectomy, with intra-operative fluoroscopic cholangiography

Anesthesia: General Anesthesia and 0.5% Marcaine (10 cc/s)

Estimated blood loss: minimal

Drains: None

Specimen: Gallbladder

Operative indications: This is a 49-year-old female with the above diagnosis who presents for elective Laparoscopy, Cholecystectomy and Intra-operative Cholangiography.

Operative procedure: The patient was brought to the OR suite with PAS stocking in place. They were transferred to the operative table, given a general anesthetic, positioned supine on the table, and the operative field was sterilely prepped and draped.

A vertical incision was made in the base of the umbilicus and deepened through the fascia. Stay sutures of 0-proline were placed and the abdomen was entered under direct vision. A Hassan canula was anchored in place with the stay sutures and the abdomen was insufflated to 15 mm Hg with CO_2 gas.

A 10 mm, 30-degree scope was assembled, focused, white-balanced and placed into the abdomen. Cursory evaluation revealed no other obvious pathology with the exception of the gallbladder. Under direct vision, 3-5 mm ports were placed in the epigastrium, right upper quadrant, and right lower quadrant. The patient was placed in reverse Trendelenberg position with right side up.

The fundus of the gallbladder was grasped and retracted over the dome of the liver. Adhesions to the gallbladder were taken down with sharp and blunt dissection while carefully maintaining hemostasis with electrocautery. The ampulla of the gallbladder was grasped with a second instrument and retracted downward and laterally displaying the angle of Calot distracted from the portal structures. The cystic duct and artery were dissected circumferentially. A single clip was placed on the distal cystic duct and an opening created just proximal to it. The cholangiogram apparatus was introduced into the abdomen via the 5 mm RUQ port and the 5-french whistle-tip ureteral catheter was threaded into the common bile duct through the opening in the cystic duct. The cholangiogram was performed under fluoroscopy and was normal, demonstrating filling of the duct with defects and prompt flow into the duodenum. The cholangiogram apparatus was withdrawn from the abdomen, and the cystic duct was clipped twice proximally and divided. The cystic artery was clipped once distally, twice proximally and divided. The cystic duct and artery were dissected circumferentially, clipped once distally, twice proximally and divided. Care was taken not to encroach upon the common bile duct or portal structures.

The gallbladder was taken down from the liver using the hook-dissector and cautery carefully maintaining hemostasis during the process. The right upper quadrant was irrigated with saline and suctioned dry. Hemostasis was confirmed. There was no bile drainage from the gallbladder bed in the liver. A 5 mm, 30-degree scope was assembled, focused, white-balanced, and placed into the epigastric port. The gallbladder was removed under direct vision through the umbilical port. The other ports were removed under direct vision and were hemostatic.

The abdomen was de-insufflated. The fascia in the umbilical incision was closed with a figure of eight suture of 0 Vicryl. The wounds were infiltrated with a total of 10 cc's of 0.5% Marcaine. The skin incisions were closed with subcuticular sutures of 4.0 Vicryl. Steri-strips and sterile dressings were applied. After a correct sponge, instrument, and needle count, the patient was awakened, extubated and taken to the recovery room in good condition.

What are the CPT® and ICD-9-CM codes reported?

Case 6

Preoperative diagnosis: Severe obesity. Hypertension. BMI 53

Postoperative diagnosis: Severe obesity. Hypertension. BMI 53

Procedure performed: Laparoscopic antecolic Roux-en-Y gastric bypass with 150 alimentary limb, and a 40 cm biliopancreatic limb.

Anesthesia: General endotracheal anesthesia.

Operative procedure: The patient was brought to the operating room, placed on the OR table in supine position. Once endotracheal anesthesia was achieved and preop antibiotics were given, the abdomen was prepped and draped in the standard surgical fashion. Access to the abdominal cavity was through a 1 cm supraumbilical incision with an Optiview trocar. CO_2 was insufflated to achieve an intraabdominal pressure of approximately 15 mm Hg. Accessory trocars were placed in the subxiphoid, right, mid and left upper quadrants of the abdomen, as well as in the right and left lower quadrants of the abdomen. All this was done under appropriate videoscopic observation.

The procedure begins with identification of the GE junction and dissection of the angle of His. On the lesser curvature of the stomach, a window is dissected into the lesser sac. A linear stapler is passed, and the stomach is transected. Reinforcement of the staple line was done with Steri-Strips, creating a pouch, which is approximately 50 cc in diameter. An Ewald tube is used to calibrate the pouch. At this point, the ligament of Treitz is identified and 40 cm from the ligament of Treitz, the small bowel was transected. The distal limb of the small bowel is then brought to the upper abdomen, and a side-to-side gastrojejunostomy between the pouch and the alimentary limb is performed with a linear stapler. The gastrojejunostomy site is then suture closed with a double layer of running 2-0 Vicryl sutures. The anastomosis was observed for leakage with air and Methylene blue. There was no evidence of leakage.

I then proceeded 150 cm distal from the gastrojejunostomy. A side-to-side jejunojejunostomy was created between the biliopancreatic limb and alimentary limb. This was performed using two applications of the linear stapler. The jejunojejunostomy site is closed with several applications of the linear stapler. Hemoclips were applied to the suture line for hemostasis. Good hemostasis was evident. A 19 French Blake drain was placed over the gastrojejunal anastomosis. All trocars were removed under appropriate videoscopic observation. There was no evidence of bleeding from any of the trocar sites. The trocar sites were suture closed and injected with local anesthesia. The patient tolerated the procedure well. She was extubated on the OR table and transferred to the recovery room in stable condition. There were no complications.

What are the CPT® and ICD-9-CM codes reported?

Case 7

Extent of examination: Upper Gastrointestinal Endoscopy

Reason(s) for examination: GERD

Description of procedure: Informed consent was obtained with the benefits, risks, and alternatives to upper GI endoscopy explained, including the risk of perforation, and the patient agreed to proceed. No contraindications were noted on physical exam. Anesthesia administered by Intensive Care Unit Staff. (See Anesthesiologist report) Monitored anesthesia care (MAC) was administered. The procedure was performed with the patient in the left lateral decubitus position. The instrument was inserted to the Second part of the duodenum. The patient tolerated the procedure well. There were no complications. The heart rate was normal. The oxygen saturation and skin color were normal. Upon discharge from the endoscopy area, the patient will be recovered per established procedures and protocols.

Findings: The esophagus was examined and no abnormalities were seen. The gastro-esophageal junction (upper level of gastric folds) was located 40 cm from the incisors. The stomach was examined and no abnormalities were seen. The small bowel was examined and no abnormalities were seen.

What are the CPT® and ICD-9-CM codes reported?

Case 8

Extent of examination: Terminal ileum

Reason(s) for examination: Anemia, Fe Deficiency

Description of procedure: Informed consent was obtained with the benefits, risks, and alternatives to colonoscopy explained, including the risk of perforation, and the patient agreed to proceed. No contraindications were noted on physical exam. Monitored anesthesia care (MAC) was administered. The bowel was prepared with GO-LYTELY Prep. The quality of the prep is based on the Ottawa bowel preparation quality scale. Total Score: Right: 1 + Middle: 1 + Left: 1 + Fluid: 0 = 3/14. Prior to the exam a digital exam was performed and hemorrhoid is noted.

The procedure was performed with the patient in the left lateral decubitus position. The instrument was inserted to the terminal ileum. The cecum was identified by the following: the ileocecal valve, the appendiceal orifice. In the rectum, a retroflex was performed. The patient tolerated the procedure well. There were no complications.

Findings: In the rectum, a few medium-size uncomplicated internal hemorrhoids were seen. The internal hemorrhoids were not bleeding. There was no evidence of inflammation, friability or granularity. Biopsy was taken. In the ascending colon and cecum there was mild granularity and red spots that were nonspecific and possibly due to air insufflation. No friability or ulcerations. Biopsy was taken. The remainder of the colon was normal. The terminal ileum was normal.

What are the CPT® and ICD-9-CM codes reported?

Case 9

Extent of examination: Terminal ileum

Reason(s) for examination: Hx of Rectal Cancer s/p LAR and colonic J pouch for closure of loop ileostomy

Description of procedure: Informed consent was obtained with the benefits, risks, and alternatives to colonoscopy explained, including the risk of perforation, and the patient agreed to proceed. No contraindications were noted on physical exam. Monitored anesthesia care (MAC) was administered. The bowel was prepared with Fleets enemas. The quality of the prep was fair. Prior to the exam a digital exam was performed and it was unremarkable. The procedure was performed with the patient in the left lateral decubitus position. The cecum was identified by the following: the ileocecal valve. The withdrawal time from the Cecum was 7 minutes. The patient tolerated the procedure well. There were no complications. The exam was limited by poor preparation.

Findings: At the splenic flexure, moderate inflammation with erythema, granularity, friability, hypervascularity was seen. There was no mucosal bleeding. In the proximal descending colon, moderate segmental inflammation with erythema, granularity, friability, hypervascularity was seen. In the rectum, an abnormality was noted:

Anastomosis—patent and normal. No evidence of polyp. Just proximal to anastomosis—significant diffuse colitis.

What are the CPT® and ICD-9-CM codes reported?

Case 10

Extent of examination: Proximal sigmoid colon

Reason(s) for examination: Proctitis

Postoperative assessment: Proctitis

Description of procedure: Informed consent was obtained with the benefits, risks, and alternatives to sigmoidoscopy explained, including the risk of perforation, and the patient agreed to proceed. No contraindications were noted on physical exam. Patient re-examined; and no interval changes noted from preoperative History & Physical. After being placed on the table, patient identification was verified prior to the procedure. Immediately prior to sedation for endoscopy the patients ASA Classification was Class 2: Mild systemic disease. Monitored anesthesia care (MAC) was administered. The quality of the prep was Adequate. Prior to the exam a digital exam was performed and it was unremarkable.

The procedure was performed with the patient in the left lateral decubitus position. The sigmoidscope was inserted to the proximal sigmoid colon. In the rectum, a retroflex was performed. The withdrawal time from the Proximal sigmoid colon was 8 minutes. The patient tolerated the procedure well.

There were no complications. The heart rate was normal. The oxygen saturation and skin color were normal. IV moderate sedation was administered under direct supervision of physician. Upon discharge from the endoscopy area, the patient will be recovered per established procedures and protocols.

Findings: In the rectum, mild segmental inflammation with erythema was seen. There was no mucosal bleeding.

What are the CPT® and ICD-9-CM codes reported?

Case 10

Extent of examination: Proximal sigmoid colon.

Reason(s) for examination: Rectitis

Postoperative assessment: Rectitis

Description of procedure: Informed consent was obtained with the benefits, risks, and alternatives in standard language explained, including the risk of perforation, and the patient agreed to proceed. No complicating conditions were noted on physical exam. Current medications and known allergies derived from the preoperative history was reviewed. After being placed on the table, patient information was reviewed prior to the procedure time out. In preparation for colonoscopy the patient was disinfected and draped. IV Versed was given. Monitored anesthesia care (MAC) was administered. The quality of the prep was adequate. Only a trace of liquid was encountered and it was suctioned off the...

The procedure was performed with the patient in the left lateral decubitus position. The sigmoidoscope was inserted to the proximal sigmoid colon. In the rectum externally, a hemorrhoid. The withdrawal time from the proximal sigmoid colon was 8 minutes. The patient tolerated the procedure well.

There were no complications. The heart rate was normal. The oxygen saturation and the color were normal. IV fluids totaling were given. After recovery, with supervision of physician. Upon discharge from the recovery area, the patient was at the accepted or established procedural times and protocols.

Findings: Rectum, mild anorectal inflammation with erythema was seen. There was no mucosal bleeding.

What are the CPT and ICD-9-CM codes reported?

Case 1

Operative Report

Preoperative diagnosis: Transitional cell carcinoma in the bladder

Postoperative diagnosis: Transitional cell carcinoma in the bladder

Procedure:	Cystoscopy; Excision bladder tumor—1 cm
	Bilateral retrograde pyelogram
	Cytology of bladder
Anesthesia:	General
Estimated blood loss:	10 cc
Complications:	None
Counts:	Correct

Indications: The patient is a 58-year-old male status post partial cystectomy for transitional cell carcinoma of the bladder. He understood the risks and benefits of today's procedure, and elected to proceed.

Procedure description: The patient was brought to the operating room and placed on the operating room table and placed in the supine position. After adequate LMA anesthesia was accomplished he was put in the dorsal lithotomy position and prepped and draped in the usual sterile fashion.

A 21-French rigid cystoscope was introduced through the urethra and a thorough cystourethroscopy was performed. A 1 cm tumor was noted on the posterior bladder wall. The tumor was resected without complications.

We obtained bladder cytology and performed a retrograde pyelogram which showed no filling defects or irregularities.

The bladder was emptied and lidocaine jelly instilled in the urethra. He was extubated and taken to the recovery room in good condition.

Disposition. The patient was taken to the post anesthesia care unit and then discharged home.

Bilateral Retrograde Pyelogram Interpretation

A bilateral retrograde pyelogram was performed which showed no filling defects or irregularities.

What are the CPT® and ICD-9-CM codes reported?

Case 2

Operative Note

Preoperative diagnosis: Gross Hematuria

Postoperative diagnosis: Bladder/prostate tumor

Operation: Transurethral resection bladder tumor (TURBT) large (5.3 cm)

Anesthesia: General

Findings: The patient had extensive involvement of the bladder with solid and edematous-appearing hemorrhagic tumor completely replacing the trigone and extending into the bladder neck and prostatic tissue. The ureteral orifices were not identifiable.

Digital rectal examination revealed nodular, firm mass per rectum.

Procedure description: The patient was placed on the operating room table in the supine position, and general anesthesia was induced. He was then placed in the lithotomy position and prepped and draped appropriately.

Cystoscopy was done which showed evidence of the urethral trauma due to the traumatic removal of the Foley catheter (patient stepped on the tubing and the catheter was pulled out). The bladder itself showed extensive clot retention. Papillary and necrotic-appearing nodular tissue mass extensively involving the trigone and the bladder neck and the prostate area. The ureteral orifices were not identified.

After consulting with the patient's wife and obtaining an adjustment to the surgical consent, the tumor was resected from the trigone, bladder neck and prostate. Obvious edematous and hemorrhagic tissue was removed. Extensive electrocauterization was done of bleeding vessels. Several areas of necrotic-appearing tissue were evacuated. Care was taken to avoid extending resection into the area of the external sphincter.

Digital rectal examination revealed the firm, nodular mass in the anterior rectum. No impacted stool was identified.

At the end of the procedure hemostasis appeared good. Tissue chips were evacuated from the bladder. Foley catheter was inserted.

Patient was taken to the recovery room in satisfactory condition.

Addendum: The patient has had a previous partial prostatectomy and had been found to have T2b N0 MX prostate cancer. On the physical examination today and on the endoscopic exam it was unclear as to whether the tumor mass was related to the bladder or recurrent prostate cancer.

Pathology revealed bladder carcinoma in the trigone and bladder neck and recurrent prostate cancer

What are the CPT® and ICD-9-CM codes reported?

Case 3

Operative Note

Preoperative diagnosis: Ta grade 3 transitional cell carcinoma (TCC) bladder CA in January 2010

Postoperative diagnosis: Ta grade 3 transitional cell carcinoma (TCC) bladder CA in January 2010; now 2 new bladder lesions

Operation:	Cystoscopy
Anesthesia:	Local

Findings: There were 2 tiny papillary lesions in the posterior wall of the bladder; otherwise the cystoscopy was negative.

Procedure description: A flexible cystoscope was introduced into the patient's urethra. A thorough cystoscopic examination was done. Bilateral ureteral orifices were visualized effluxing clear yellow urine. All sides of the bladder were inspected, and retroflexion was performed. Cytology was sent.

Plan: We will schedule the patient for a bladder biopsy at the next-available date.

Case 4

Operative Note

Preoperative diagnosis: Desire for circumcision

Postoperative diagnosis: Desire for circumcision

Procedure: Circumcision

Anesthesia: General

Indications: The patient is a 19-year-old white male, sexually active for 2 years. He requests circumcision. He understands the risks and benefits of circumcision.

Procedure description: The patient was brought to the operating room and placed on the operating room table in the supine position. After adequate LMA anesthesia was accomplished he was given a dorsal penile block and a modified ring block with 0.25% Marcaine plain.

Two circumferential incisions were made around the patient's penis to allow for the maximal aesthetic result. Adequate hemostasis was then achieved with the Bovie, and the skin edges were reapproximated using 4-0 chromic simple interrupted sutures with a U-stitch at the frenulum.

The patient was extubated and taken to the recovery room in good condition.

Disposition: The patient was taken to the post anesthesia care unit and then discharged home.

What are the CPT® and ICD-9-CM codes reported?

Case 5

Operative Report

Preoperative diagnosis: Rt ureteral stones

Postoperative diagnosis: Rt ureteral stones

Operation: Open right ureterolithotomy

Intraoperative findings: The patient had marked inflammatory reaction around the proximal ureter just below the renal pelvis. Multiple stone fragments were embedded in the edematous ureteral lining.

Procedure: The patient was placed on the operating room table in the supine position. General anesthesia was induced. He was then placed in a right flank up position. An incision was made off the tip of the 12th rib and dissection carried down through skin, fat, and fascia to open the lumbodorsal fascia entering the retroperitoneal space. The peritoneum was swept anteriorly.

Careful dissection was then carried down in the retroperitoneal space to first identify the vena cava and then identify the renal vein and then with these structures localized, the ureter was identified.

Careful dissection was done to mobilize the ureter and identify the area of the stone impaction by palpation.

The ureter was then opened longitudinally and ureteral stent was identified. The multiple stone fragments were then removed from the ureteral lumen. The ureteral lumen was then irrigated copiously and no other stone fragments were identifiable.

The ureterotomy was then reapproximated with interrupted sutures of 5-0 chromic.

Inspection showed good hemostasis.

Sponge and needle counts were correct, and closure was begun after placement of a Blake drain through separate inferior stab wound. Marcaine 0.5% with no epinephrine was used to infiltrate the intercostal nerves. The wound was then closed in layers with muscle and fascial approximation with #1 Vicryl. The skin was closed with staples. Sterile dressings were applied.

The patient returned to recovery area in satisfactory condition.

What are the CPT® and ICD-9-CM codes reported for this procedure?

Case 6

Operative Report

Preoperative diagnosis: Prostate Cancer

Postoperative diagnosis: Prostate Cancer

Procedure: Radical retropubic prostatectomy with bilateral pelvic lymph node dissection.

Statement of medical necessity: The patient is a very pleasant 58-year-old gentleman with Gleason 7 prostate cancer. He understood the risks and benefits of radical retropubic prostatectomy including failure to cure, recurrence of cancer, need for future procedures, impotence, and incontinence. He understood these risks and he elected to proceed.

Statement of operation: The patient was brought to the operating room and placed on the operating table in the supine position. After adequate general endotracheal anesthesia was accomplished, he was put in the dorsal lithotomy position and he was prepped and draped in the usual sterile fashion. A 20 French Foley catheter was introduced in the patient's urethra and the balloon was inflated with 20 ml of sterile water.

We made a midline infraumbilical incision and dissected down to the rectus fascia. We then transected the rectus fascia between the bellies of the rectus muscle and dissected into the retropubic space. We placed a Bookwalter retractor to aid in visualization and to protect the surrounding structures. We did bilateral pelvic lymph node dissection, taking care to avoid the hypogastric and obturator nerves bilaterally. The node packets were sent off the field for permanent section and frozen section. We then dissected the prostate free from its lateral side wall and dorsal attachments superficially and placed a right angle clamp behind the dorsal venous complex and tied off the dorsal venous complex with 2 free ties of #1 Vicryl. We sewed some back bleeding sutures over the prostate and we placed a right angle again behind the dorsal venous complex and then transected it with a long handled blade. We carefully inspected the dorsal venous complex for any bleeding and no bleeding was noted. We then placed a right angle clamp behind the urethra and transected the anterior aspect of the urethra, exposing the Foley catheter. We grasped this with a tonsil and then cut off the Foley catheter at the urethral meatus and pulled the Foley catheter into the urethral incision that had been made. We then transected the posterior urethra, freeing the prostate from its apical attachment. This allowed us to apply upward retraction to the prostate and dissect it free from the rectal anterior wall. We then clipped and cut the lateral pedicles to free the prostate up to the level of the bladder neck. We then transected Denonvilliers' fascia and identified the bilateral vas deferens, which were clipped and cut accordingly. We also dissected the seminal vesicles leaving the tips of the seminal vesicles in place in the hopes of improving his continence.

Once this was complete, we dissected the prostate free from the bladder neck using electrocautery. Once we had opened the anterior aspect of the bladder, we were able to identify the bilateral ureteral orifices effluxing indigo carmine that had been administered about 10 minutes earlier by the anesthesiologist. Once the prostate was sent off the field for permanent section, we turned our attention to recapitulating the bladder neck. We everted the bladder mucosa with 4-0 Monocryl and then closed the bladder neck in a tennis racquet closure using 2-0 Vicryl. We then placed a Roth sound in the patient's urethra after ensuring adequate hemostasis in the pelvis and placed 5 anastomotic sutures of 2-0 Monocryl surrounding the urethra. We then placed them in the corresponding location in the bladder neck after a Foley catheter, 20 French in size, had been placed through the urethra and into the bladder and the balloon was inflated with 20 ml of sterile water. We then cinched down these anastomotic sutures and tied them off. We irrigated the Foley catheter and ensured that there was no bladder leak. We then placed a JP drain in the patient's left lateral quadrant, taking care to avoid the epigastric vessels. We stitched the drain in place with a 2-0 silk. We closed the fascia with #1 Vicryl in a running fashion and closed the subcutaneous tissues with 3-0 Vicryl. The skin was stapled closed and a sterile dressing was applied and his catheter was again irrigated with return of blue urine. No clots.

The patient was extubated, taken to the recovery room in good condition.

What are the CPT® and ICD-9-CM codes reported?

Case 7

Operative Note

Preoperative diagnosis: Left renal calculus

Postoperative diagnosis: Left renal calculus

Procedure: ESWL 2300 shocks at 22kV.

Description of procedure: After the KUB was reviewed revealing a lower caliceal calculi on the left, the patient was anesthetized and positioned on the lithotripsy table. The stone was targeted and treated with 60 shocks for 2 minutes and then a 2 minute pause was carried out. We then resumed at 60 slowly working up to 120, for a total of 1800 shocks on the lower pole, which completely disappeared. We then shocked the tip of the stent with 500 shocks as calcification was seen there on the prior KUB, but it was unclear on today's KUB where with fluoro whether that was still present. The patient appeared to tolerate the procedure well and was brought to recovery room in stable condition. He will follow up in 1 week for possible stent removal, KUB prior to procedure.

What are the CPT® and ICD-9-CM codes reported?

Case 8

Operative Note

Preoperative diagnosis: Prostate cancer

Postoperative diagnosis: Prostate cancer

Procedure: Ultrasound guidance placement of gold fiducial markers

Description of procedure: The patient is a 62-year-old male with prostate cancer. He is to undergo external beam radiation therapy, and radiation oncology asked me to place the fiducial gold markers. Informed consent was obtained. The patient was brought to the procedure room. He received oral sedation prior to the procedure. Ultrasound was performed and utilizing 20 ml of lidocaine, the prostate were numbed with lidocaine. Next, position markers were placed at the right and left bases, as well as the left apex of the prostate gland without difficulty. He had an excellent appearance and ultrasound. The patient did not suffer any pain or other problems during the procedure. The hospital ultrasound department assisted me in imaging.

What are the CPT® and ICD-9-CM codes reported?

Case 9

Operative Note

Preoperative diagnosis:

1. Large right inguinal hernia
2. Bilateral undescended testes

Postoperative Diagnosis:

1. Bilateral inguinal hernias
2. Undescended testes

Procedure performed: Bilateral orchiopexy and bilateral inguinal hernia repairs as well as circumcision on a 10 year-old-patient

Estimated blood loss: Less than 5 ml

Complications: None

Description of procedure: After informed consent had been obtained previously and reviewed again in the preoperative area, the patient was brought back to the OR, placed supine and general anesthesia was induced without problems. It was somewhat difficult to find an IV site, because of the patient's body habitus. However, there were no complications with anesthesia. The patient was then appropriately padded and prepped and draped in sterile fashion. 0.25% Marcaine plain was used for bilateral inguinal blocks as well as injected in the sub-q in the inguinal crease. I began on the right hand side where he had an intermittent right inguinal bulge for several months. A scalpel was used to make a skin incision following the creases and this was extended down through very generous subcutaneous fat and Scarpa's to expose the external oblique aponeurosis. The external ring was identified as was the ilioinguinal ligament. The ring was opened for a short distance. The testis was high in the scrotum and was brought through. The gubernaculum was then divided. A very large hernia sac was carefully opened and then very carefully dissected down to the level of the internal ring. There did not appear to be any abdominal contents within the hernia sac. It was then twisted and suture ligated at the base. The hernia sac was then sent to pathology. The testis was pink and viable. A dartos pouch was created and the testis brought through it. The neck of the pouch was tightened with a few interrupted sutures of 3-0 Vicryl. Care was taken to make sure it did not twist the testicle that the testis lay in a normal anatomical position. The scrotal incision was then closed with 5-0 plain gut. The external ring was recreated by approximating the aponeurosis of the external oblique. The underlying ilioinguinal nerve was identified and spared. Scarpa's was approximated with 3-0 Vicryl and the skin closed with 5-0 Monocryl in a running subcuticular stitch. Steri-Strips and dressing were placed over this.

On the left hand side initially his testis was felt to be almost nonpalpable but on exam under anesthesia it again was within the high scrotum. With gentle pressure, I could make this essentially disappear into his abdomen suggesting a large communicating hydrocele. Therefore, I made the decision to proceed with inguinal hernia repair and exploration. Again, he had a Marcaine inguinal block and the skin was also anesthetized with 0.25% Marcaine. A matching incision was made with a scalpel following the skin creases. This was extended down through subcutaneous tissues and Scarpas to expose the external oblique and the external ring. It was then twisted and suture ligated at the base with 3-0 Vicryl. The hernia sac was also sent to pathology. At this point, there was sufficient length to easily bring the testis into the scrotum. A Dartos pouch was created and the testis was brought into it with care taken to make sure we did not twist the cord structures. The neck of the pouch was tightened with 3-0 Vicryl and then the scrotal incision closed with 5-0 plain gut in an identical fashion. The external oblique was approximated with a few interrupted sutures of 3-0 Vicryl to recreate the ring. Again, care was taken to preserve the underlying ilioinguinal nerve. Scarpa's was approximated 3-0 Vicryl as well and the skin closed with Monocryl. Steri-Strips and dressing were placed over this as well.

0.25% Marcaine plain was then used for a penile block. A circumcising incision was made approximately 3 mm below the coronal margin and the penis partially degloved. Meticulous hemostasis obtained with Bovie cautery. The excess prepuce was trimmed. It was then discarded. The skin edges were approximated with 5-0 plain gut in a running fashion x 2. Hemostasis was excellent. The glans head appeared normal. A dressing of conform and Vaseline gauze was applied. The patient was then extubated and sent to the recovery in stable condition. No complications.

What are the CPT® and ICD-9-CM codes reported?

Case 10

Operative Note

Preoperative diagnosis:

1. Intrinsic sphincter deficiency
2. Incontinence

Postoperative diagnosis:

1. Intrinsic sphincter deficiency
2. Incontinence

Procedure: Cystoscopy with Durasphere injection

Estimated blood loss: Less than 5 cc

Complications: None

Counts: Correct

Indications: This is a very pleasant female with intrinsic sphincter deficiency causing urinary incontinence. She understood the risks and benefits of the procedure and she elected to proceed.

Procedure description: The patient was brought to the operating room and placed on the operating room table in the supine position. After adequate LMA anesthesia was accomplished she was prepped and draped in the usual sterile fashion.

A 21-French cystoscope was introduced in the patient's urethra. Her urethra was fairly pale, not well approximated, and was patulous. We injected 2½ syringes of Durasphere material into the urethra but were unable to get anymore than that amount into the tissue. There was moderate approximation of the urethral mucosa.

The bladder was emptied and lidocaine jelly instilled. She was extubated and taken to the recovery room in good condition.

Disposition: The patient was taken to the post anesthesia care unit and then discharged home.

What are the CPT® and ICD-9-CM codes reported?

Case 1

Diagnoses: Stage III cystocele, stage II uterine prolapse.

Procedure: Pessary fitting.

Indications: A 75-year-old, gravida 2, para 2, female with pelvic organ prolapse. She had atrophic vaginitis so we had her use Premarin vaginal cream twice a week for 6 weeks. She is back for a pessary fitting today.

Findings: She has a third-degree cystocele, and now third-degree uterine prolapse. Her vaginal tissues are improved, although still atrophic, but much less thin than prior appointment. She has a stage I, rectocele.

Description of procedure: After her exam, I started with a #4 ring pessary with support. This was clearly not large enough and the cystocele was coming around it. I then went to a #5 ring pessary with support with the same problem. I went to the #6 ring pessary with support. It did not lodge behind her pubic bone very well, but it definitely reduced all of her prolapse. She mentioned earlier in the appointment that she could not void when she came in today. She has not tried reducing it. I am hopeful that the pessary may help with that. The #6 was comfortable for her. I stood her up and put her through some maneuvers and it stayed nicely in place. Then she went walking with it in for 10 or 15 minutes and went up and down the stairs. She definitely was able to void easily with that in. It was comfortable and she did not really notice it was in.

On recheck it still seemed like she had a little more room in the pelvis. I removed the #6 and went up to a #7 size. This seemed to reduce the prolapse a bit better, but was a little uncomfortable for her. We went back to the #6 ring pessary with support. She was able to remove it and place it with instruction in our clinic today.

Disposition: We have ordered the #6 ring pessary with support and it will be sent to her. After she gets the pessary, she will remove it once a week and leave it out over night. She will continue to use the Premarin vaginal cream twice a week. She will return to clinic after she has used the pessary for 2 or 3 weeks, so we can check her tissues. She is to report if she has vaginal discharge or bleeding, as she is at risk for getting ulceration from the pessary.

I answered all of her questions about her condition of pelvic organ prolapse and treatment with estrogen and pessary. She will call if she has any bleeding.

What are the CPT® and ICD-9-CM codes reported?

Case 2

Diagnoses:

1. Complete procidentia
2. Recurrent urinary tract infections
3. Postmenopausal vaginal bleeding

Procedures:

1. Vaginal hysterectomy
2. Anterior and posterior colporrhaphy
3. Cystoscopy
4. Vaginal vault suspension

Specimens: Uterus and cervix.

Findings: A thick hypertrophic ulcerated cervix was noted. The adnexa were small and atrophic. Complete procidentia with cystocele and rectocele. Cystoscopy done after indigo carmine, at the end of the case, revealed bilateral strong ureteral jets.

Indications: Pt. with history of postmenopausal vaginal bleeding, anemia and recurrent urinary tract infections, although she denied any urinary incontinence. Her cervix was found to be ulcerated, erythematous and hypertrophic. Cervical biopsy was negative for neoplasia but the endometrial biopsy showed evidence of active endometritis. She desires surgical management of these problems.

Operation: The patient was taken to the operating room and placed in lithotomy position while awake. The patient has a history of bilateral knee replacements and cannot bend her legs so we did put her in lithotomy position using Yellofin stirrups, but kept her legs without any bend and positioned her while she was awake in a comfortable way. The patient was then placed under general anesthesia. An exam under anesthesia was done with findings of a complete procidentia with ulcerations posteriorly. The vagina and perineum was prepped in the usual sterile fashion. A tenaculum was then placed on the right and left lateral cervix. A circumferential incision was made at the cervicovaginal junction using Bovie cautery. The vesicovaginal fascia was then dissected anteriorly using a combination of sharp dissection with Metzenbaum scissors and blunt dissection.

Attention was then turned posteriorly. The posterior peritoneum was grasped with a half curve, identified a then incised using Mayo scissors. A weighted speculum was then placed in the posterior cul de sac. The uterosacral ligaments were identified and clamped bilaterally with Heaney clamps, and a transection suture using 0 Vicryl suture was placed at the tip of the clamp system in both the right and left side. The uterocervical ligaments were then tagged and held for use during the vaginal vault suspension.

Attention was then turned to the anterior peritoneum. A finger was placed in the posterior cul de sac up around the uterine fundus distending the anterior vaginal epithelium and allowing the anterior peritoneum could be entered safely using Mayo scissors. The cardinal ligaments were clamped and cut bilaterally. The utero-ovarian were identified cut, suture-ligated, and then free tied bilaterally. The uterus was then removed from the vagina and sent to pathology. All pedicles were then inspected and were found to be hemostatic. We could not visualize the ovaries but were palpated and felt to be atrophic.

At this point, we began the vaginal vault suspension. There was some oozing from the patient's left side near the vaginal cuff area. This was controlled with a figure-of-eight suture of 0 Polysorb. Other small areas along the cuff were touched with the Bovie, and hemostasis was very good at this point. The uterosacral ligament remnant was put under pressure to palpate the ligament through its course to near the ischial spine. The bladder was drained with a Foley. A long Allis clamp was placed on the uterosacral near the ischial spine by tugging gently on the remnant that was stretched out and using the more inferior fibers. A suture of 0 Polysorb was placed through the ligament with care to drive the needle from superior to inferior, to avoid the ureter. A second suture was placed slightly more distal with 0 Maxon and then more distal again a 0 Polysorb. These were all held while a similar procedure was repeated on the left side with palpation of the ligament and the ischial spine and taking the inferior fibers.

All of the sutures were held while the anterior and posterior repairs were made. The anterior vagina was then inspected and the cystocele identified. The vaginal wall was trimmed anteriorly. The posterior vagina was also inspected and excessive tissue was excised. At this point the vaginal cuff appeared hemostatic and was closed by first taking the 0 Polysorb, which is the distal uterosacral stitch and making an angle stitch to close the vagina. The anterior and posterior vaginal walls were closed as well as the pubocervical fascia anteriorly and the rectovaginal fascia posteriorly to get fascia to fascia closure. Once each of the angle stitches had been placed, they were held and not tied down yet. The 0 Maxon were then placed in a similar fashion through the anterior vaginal fascia and mucosa and the posterior fascia and mucosa. Lastly the 0 Prolene, which were the most superior stitches, were placed through the anterior posterior vaginal cuff, but these were taken slightly away from the cut edge so that the knots could be buried but again taking fascia and vaginal mucosa. Then a 0 Polysorb figure-of-eight suture was placed across the midline and vaginal mucosa so that we could completely bury the Prolene sutures at the end of the case. At this point, all of the sutures were tied except the Polysorb to close the mucosa in the midline. There appeared to be excellent vaginal support at this point.

The Foley catheter was removed. The 17-French cystoscope sheath was placed through the urethra. The 70 degree lens was used with sterile water infusing to inspect the bladder. There was moderate trabeculation of the bladder. There were no mucosal lesions to explain her infections. There were no stones, stitches or other lesions. A quarter of an ampule of indigo carmine had been given about 10 minutes earlier IV. Strong ureteral jets were observed from both sides, although the right side concentrated the dye faster than the left side by about 5 minutes. The bladder was drained and the urethra was inspected with the 0 degree lens and there were no urethral lesions. The bladder was drained and the Foley catheter replaced.

The last midline 0 Polysorb suture was closed over the midline to bury the Prolene. All the sutures were cut and the cuff had been irrigated with the cystoscopy fluid. A rectal exam was done, which did not yield any sutures. The vagina was then irrigated and was found to be hemostatic. A vaginal pack was then placed. The patient was awakened from general anesthesia and brought to the PACU in stable condition.

What are the CPT® and ICD-9-CM codes?

Case 3

Indications: 21-year-old, G3, P1-0-2-1, found to have an abnormal cervical Pap test with possible LGSIL. She presents for follow up Pap and colposcopy

Exam: Pubic hair is shaved. Negative inguinal adenopathy. The urethra, the introitus and anus grossly normal. Vagina is long, need extra long Pederson speculum. Cervix is posterior, parous. Uterus anteverted, normal size. Some tenderness of the adnexa to deep palpation. No cervical motion tenderness. Normal discharge. Pap test was performed.

Colposcopic procedure: Speculum was inserted for the colposcopy. An extra long, narrow Pederson speculum was required and the cervix was visualized. 3% acetic acid was placed and the T-zone is large and bleeds to touch. The 3% acetic acid was placed, and several aceto-white lesions were noted, particularly at the 12 and 11 o'clock positions. Lugol solution was placed, and there was no uptake at the 6 and 11 o'clock portions of the cervix. 4% topical lidocaine was placed without epinephrine, followed by 1 cc of 1% lidocaine also without epinephrine. LEEP biopsy was taken of the cervix without difficulty and this also cauterized the bleeding.

Instructions given to the patient that she must refrain from intercourse for at least 1 week. She is aware to call if any severe pain, bleeding that does not stop, foul odor, or fever. She is aware the results will take approximately 1–2 weeks and she will receive direct notification.

What are the CPT® and ICD-9-CM codes?

Case 4

Chief complaint: Contraceptive placement of IUD

Indications: Ms. Barrett is coming into the office for placement of an IUD. She is a 29-year-old, gravida 1, para 1-0-0-1 who is status post a normal spontaneous vaginal delivery of a male infant weighing 4086 grams. She has not had intercourse since delivery. She is interested in a Mirena IUD at this time.

Procedure: After obtaining consent, the patient is placed in the dorsal lithotomy position. A speculum was placed in the vagina to visualize the cervix. The cervix was cleaned 3 times with Betadine. Following this, a single-tooth tenaculum was placed on the anterior lip of the cervix. The uterus was sounded to approximately 6.5 cm. The Mirena IUD was then placed in the usual fashion and the strings cut to 2.5 cm. The lot number is TU003SL. The patient tolerated the procedure well, and hemostasis was noted at the tenaculum site after removal.

The patient tolerated the procedure well and was given instructions to return if she should have any difficulties.

What are the CPT® and ICD-9-CM codes?

Case 5

ABC Hospital

Indication: A 30-year-old G0P0Ab0 with irregular periods and mild male factor. She is infertile and would like to start a clomid/iui cycle and requires hysterosalpingogram for evaluation.

Procedure Note: The patient was brought to the outpatient surgical suite. After written consent was obtained and written final verification, the cervix was visualized with a Pedersen speculum, anesthetized with Cetacaine spray and swabbed with 3 swabs of Betadine scrub and an endocervical prep.

A single-tooth tenaculum was placed on the anterior lip of the cervix without problems. An HSG catheter was introduced through the cervix. At this point the balloon was insufflated with 1 mL of normal saline within the cervix, speculum was then removed. Ethiodol contrast, approximately 8 ml, was insufflated under fluoroscopic guidance.

Under fluoroscopic guidance, the uterus shape was found to be normal. The tubes filled and spilled on the left. The right tube filled normally but no spill could be documented due to exuberant spill from the left. The patient was instructed to roll completely for two revolutions. An additional film was taken which showed normal dispersion.

Plan: Follow-up as scheduled.

What are the CPT® and ICD-9-CM codes?

Case 6

Procedure performed: Amniocentesis.

Indications: The patient is a 28-year-old G4 P2103 at 36 2/7, here in the office today for amniocentesis for FLM secondary to Rh isoimmunization to D antigen. Following informed consent she elected to proceed with the amniocentesis.

Procedure: An ultrasound was carried out that revealed a single intrauterine gestation of 36+2 weeks in vertex presentation. A site for amniocentesis was identified in the left upper uterine segment, which did not transgress the placenta and an image was retained for the record. The amniocentesis site was sterilely prepped and draped with a sterile towel and an alcohol based solution. Following this using direct ultrasound guidance a 22 gauge amniocentesis needle was sharply inserted in the amniotic fluid cavity. This returned clear amniotic fluid. 20 cc was easily aspirated and 10 cc sent for FLM and 10 cc held for possible OD450 if needed. The patient tolerated the procedure very well and fetal cardiac activity was seen following the procedure. The patient was sent for a follow-up NST. Rhogam is not indicated as the patient is already sensitized.

What are the CPT® and ICD-9-CM codes?

Case 7

OB Delivery Note

Indications: 31 y/o G3P1 at 39 and 4/7 weeks admitted in labor. She has been followed in the OB clinic with 12 normal antenatal visits.

Stage I: Patient was admitted with a cervical exam of 3/c/-1. She slowly progressed to 5 cm dilation. She had SROM at 0330 which showed light meconium. She continued to labor and reached the end of stage I at 1000, a period of 10 hours. FHTs showed some periods of reactivity but responded to stimulation.

Stage II: Duration of Stage II (from pushing to delivery) was approximately 3 hours. A pediatric team was present. There was slight meconium staining present at delivery. Presentation was OP with right shoulder anterior shoulder. There was no nuchal cord. The cord was clamped x2 and cut and the baby was handed to the pediatric team.

Gender: Male

Weight: 3772 grams. Apgars 8 /9

Stage III: Placenta delivered spontaneously with gentle traction and fundal massage and was intact. Vagina and cervix examined for lacerations. Inspection revealed a small 2nd degree perineal laceration which was repaired with 3.0 Polysorb in the usual sterile fashion in layers. Another small lateral cutaneous tear was repaired with 3.0 polysorb and a figure of 8 stitch. Good hemostasis was noted.

Patient will return to clinic for follow up in 6 weeks.

What are the CPT® and ICD-9-CM codes?

Case 8

Diagnosis: Intrauterine pregnancy at 20-5/7 weeks with multiple fetal anomalies.

Procedure: D&E

Anesthesia: Moderate sedation.

Indications: The patient is a 29-year-old gravida 1 at 20-5/7 weeks with multiple fetal anomalies, who desires a termination of pregnancy. She has previously had dilators placed.

Description of procedure: The patient was brought to the operating room, and moderate sedation was administered. The patient then placed in the dorsal lithotomy position and was prepped and draped in usual sterile fashion.

The dilators were removed. The patient's cervix was dilated to 5–6 cm. There was a bulging bag that ruptured during vaginal prep. A speculum was attempted to be placed, but the fetus was already delivering into the vagina. The umbilical cord was severed at this time, and no fetal heart beat was noted on ultrasound. Ultrasound guidance was used for the entire procedure. Gentle traction was applied and the fetus delivered intact. There was no respiratory or cardiac effort noted. Bierer forceps were then used to remove the placenta intact. A speculum was placed, and an atraumatic tenaculum was placed on the anterior lip of the cervix and a standard D&C was then performed until the characteristically gritty texture was noted on the endometrium. There was a small amount of bleeding noted from the lower uterine segment; 20 units of Pitocin was added to the patient's IV fluids and pressure was held against lower uterine segment for 5 minutes. At this time, hemostasis was noted to be excellent. The speculum was then removed, and the patient was taken out of the dorsal lithotomy position after her perineum was cleansed.

The patient's anesthesia was discontinued and she was brought to the recovery room in stable condition. There were no complications to this procedure. The patient tolerated the procedure well.

Specimen(s): The products of conception were sent to pathology for cytogenetics and pathologic evaluation.

Plan: The patient will follow up in the outpatient clinic

What are the CPT® and ICD-9-CM codes?

Case 9

Anesthesia: General with LMA.

Preoperative diagnosis: Sterilization

Postoperative diagnosis: Sterilization

Procedure performed: Tubal ligation with bilateral Falope ring application.

Counts: Needle, sponge and instrument counts were correct.

Intraoperative medications: 0.25% Marcaine with epinephrine.

Operative findings: The left ovary was mildly adhered to the side of the uterus. The right ovary appeared normal. Both tubes appeared normal. The upper abdomen appeared normal. There was a small subserosal fibroid approximately 1 to 1.5 cm on the left upper aspect of the uterus.

Description of procedure: After informed consent, Ms. Mathews was taken to operating suite #4 and a general anesthetic was administered. She was placed in the dorsal lithotomy position. She was sterilely prepped and draped in the usual manner. A sponge stick was placed vaginally. An infraumbilical incision was made and a non-bladed trocar and sheath were placed under direct visualization. Proper placement was confirmed with insufflation performed. A suprapubic incision was then made and the suprapubic trocar and sheath were placed. Findings were made as noted above and the right tube was ligated with the Falope ring, and then the left. Pictures were taken to document proper placement.

All instruments were removed and gas was allowed to escape. The sheaths were removed. Marcaine with epinephrine were placed again at the incision sites and they were closed with Monocryl in a subcuticular manner.

The patient was allowed to emerge from the anesthetic and was transferred to the Postanesthesia Care Unit in stable condition.

What are the CPT® and ICD-9-CM codes?

Case 10

Preoperative diagnosis: Severe cervical dysplasia

Postoperative diagnosis: Severe cervical dysplasia

Procedure performed: Cold knife conization.

Anesthesia: General.

Complications: None.

Estimated Blood Loss: 25 cc.

Fluids: 500 cc crystalloid.

Drains: Straight catheter x 1.

Indications: All risks, benefits, and alternatives of this procedure were discussed with the patient and informed consent was obtained.

Description of procedure: The patient was taken to the operating room where general anesthesia was obtained without difficulty. She was prepped and draped in the normal sterile fashion after being placed in the dorsal lithotomy position.

Attention was turned to the patient's pelvis where a weighted speculum was placed inside the patient's vagina. The anterior lip of the cervix was grasped with a single-tooth tenaculum and a paracervical block was performed using 10 units of Pitressin and 20 cc of normal saline. A #2-0 Vicryl stitch was used at the three o'clock and nine o'clock positions on the cervix to ligate the cervical branch of the uterine artery.

Procedure (continued): A #11 blade was then used to incise in a circumferential fashion. This incision was carried down to the cervix using a cone shape. The cervical biopsy was removed and marked at the twelve o'clock position using a silk suture.

The cervical bed was cauterized using the Bovie cautery with good hemostasis noted. The FloSeal was placed into the cervical bed and the cervical stitches were tied together in the midline. Good hemostasis was noted.

All instruments were removed from the patient's vagina. All sponge, needle and instrument counts were correct x 2.

The patient was taken out of the dorsal lithotomy position and taken to the recovery room awake and in stable condition.

What are the CPT® and ICD-9-CM codes reported?

Case 1

Preoperative diagnosis: Right thyroid follicular lesion.

Postoperative diagnosis: Right thyroid follicular lesion.

Operative procedure: Right thyroid lobectomy.

Findings: A large thyroid mass in the inferior aspect of the right thyroid. The right recurrent laryngeal nerve was identified intact and there were bilateral movements of vocal cords post procedure.

Description of operative procedure:
The patient was identified as and taken to the operating room. She was placed in a supine reverse Trendelenburg position on the operating table. Once adequate sedation was given the patient was intubated. The neck was the prepped and draped in a standard surgical fashion. Using a #15 blade, a linear incision was made approximately two centimeters above the sternal notch. This incision was carried through subcutaneous tissues and through the platysma until the anterior jugular veins were identified. Superior and inferior flaps were then created using electrocautery. A midline incision was then made separating the strap muscles. Once the thyroid was encountered, the right thyroid lobe was dissected free from the surrounding tissues. Using the harmonic scalpel, the superior, medial and inferior vessels were divided. Using the harmonic scalpel, the isthmus was then divided free from the left thyroid lobe. The recurrent laryngeal nerve on the right side was identified and not touched during the case. The left thyroid lobe was explored revealing a single nodule. The right thyroid was then completely removed from the trachea and the surrounding tissues. It was marked and then sent off the table as a specimen. The cavity was then irrigated with saline and hemostasis was achieved using electrocautery. The fascia and the strap muscles were then approximated using 3-0 Vicryl suture and a drain was placed into the cavity exiting the left aspect of the incision. The platysma was then reapproximated using 3-0 Vicryl suture. The skin was then reapproximated using 4-0 Monocryl suture in 8, running subcuticular closure and covered with Dermabond. By the end of the procedure, the sponge, needle and instrument counts were correct. The patient was extubated observing bilateral movement of the vocal cords.

What are the CPT® and ICD-9-CM codes reported?

Case 2

Preoperative diagnosis: Papillary thyroid cancer.

Postoperative diagnosis: Papillary thyroid cancer.

Operative procedure: Near total thyroidectomy.

Anesthesia: General endotracheal.

Findings: Nodular right thyroid with parathyroids visualized.

Estimated blood loss: Approximately 100 cc.

Description of operative procedure:
The patient was identified and taken to the operating room. She was placed in the supine position on the operating table. Once adequate sedation was given, the patient was intubated. A towel was placed behind the patient's shoulder blades and the neck slightly extended. The neck was prepped and draped in the standard surgical fashion. Using a #15 blade, the patient's old incision was excised. The incision was carried down through subcutaneous tissue. The superior and inferior flaps were created and using electrocautery, a midline incision was made. Once the strap muscles were identified, using blunt dissection, a plane was developed in between the strap muscle, and the right thyroid. The right thyroid appeared nodular. Using blunt dissection and electrocautery, the right thyroid lobe was freed from surrounding tissues and removed. Using the harmonic scalpel, two-thirds of the left thyroid lobe was removed sparing the parathyroids and staying clear from the recurrent laryngeal nerve. Once this was completed, hemostasis was achieved using electrocautery and Surgicel. Due to some bleeding around the parathyroid gland, Gelfoam and thrombin were placed over this area and the bleeding had subsided. A round JP drain was then placed around the remaining thyroid tissue. The strap muscles were reapproximated using interrupted 3-0 Vicryl suture. The platysma was reapproximated using interrupted 3-0 Vicryl suture and the skin was reapproximated using 4-0 Monocryl suture in an interrupted fashion and covered with Dermabond. By the end of the procedure, the sponge, needle and instrument counts were correct. The patient was then transferred to the recovery room in stable condition.

What are the CPT® and ICD-9-CM codes reported for the primary surgeon?

Case 3

Operative report

Preoperative diagnosis: Papillary carcinoma of the thyroid

Postoperative diagnosis: Papillary carcinoma of the left thyroid
                                 Lymph nodes exhibiting metastasis

Procedure: 85% thyroidectomy (subtotal)

Indications:

The patient is a 43-year-old white female patient who was referred with a history of having been diagnosed in the fall of 2006 with a papillary carcinoma of the thyroid. Thyroidectomy was recommended to her; however due to the fact that she had no insurance, it became quite obvious that she was going to have a difficult time being cared for in another state where she was at the time. She returned to this area and came to the office. We completed her workup including PET scanning, sestamibi scan for metastatic disease, etc. I recommended to her that we proceed with a subtotal thyroidectomy, i.e. 85% resection of the thyroid; however if we could isolate any parathyroids and preserve them, then we would to a total thyroidectomy. She appears to understand and is amenable to this and is willing to proceed.

Procedure:

The patient was placed on the operating room table in the supine position, neck slightly hyperextended and the table tilted in reverse Trendelenburg. The neck and anterior chest were prepped and draped in the usual sterile fashion. The incision was to be made two fingerbreadths above the sternal notch. Actually there was a fold in her skin at this level and we simply followed this natural fold from the anterior border of the left sternocleidomastoid around to the anterior border on the right. This was deepened down through the subcutaneous tissue through the platysma muscle and then flaps were created both superior and inferior to the incision, inferiorly to the sternal notch and superiorly well over and above the thyroid cartilage. At this point, it was quite apparent that the left lobe of the thyroid was rock hard, entirely a different feel from that of the right lobe.

We began on the left side with mobilization of the interior pole. Vessels were serially clamped, cut, ligated, on the thyroid side. Sutures were placed for traction at the point of clamping, staying inside these vessels. The vessels were closed with a suture ligature of 3-0 Silk. As the thyroid was mobilized, the recurrent laryngeal nerve was identified and avoided throughout the course of the dissection. There was a small lymph node attached to the side of the gland which appeared to be metastatic disease. This was obviously included with the specimen sent to pathology for confirmation. We also removed several enlarged lymph nodes. The inferior pole was entirely mobilized, and then the middle thyroid vessels were dealt with as well, staying well away from the recurrent laryngeal nerve. Then the superior pole vessels were likewise clamped, cut, and ligated. This allowed us to divide the isthmus on the right lobe side of the midline and then removed the left lobe without difficulty. There was one small bleeding vessel on or immediately adjacent to the recurrent laryngeal nerve, therefore a Surgicel packing was applied to this area and bleeding controlled.

Then dissection began on the right side where we encountered a lesion toward the trachea which was half the size of a yellow pencil eraser and could have passed for a parathyroid. Biopsies of this were taken; however they returned simply fatty tissues. We mobilized the right lobe of the thyroid and left approximately 10% of the right lobe of the thyroid intact at the superior end of the right thyroid lobe. When the portion of the lobe was amputated, we controlled the bleeding from the raw edge of the thyroid with multiple suture ligatures of 3-0 silk. Once hemostasis was secure, the procedure was terminated.

Hemostasis was secure throughout the wound. A 10 mm Jackson-Pratt drain was placed through a separate stab wound and left to lay in the midline or slightly to the left of the midline in the thyroid cavity. Strap muscles were closed in the midline with multiple interrupted figure-of-eight sutures of 2-0 Vicryl. The platysma muscle was closed with 2-0 Vicryl and the skin closed with a continuous running subcuticular closure of 3-0 Monocryl. Dermabond was applied to the wound, drain secured with a 0 silk and a small gauze dressing.

Prior to leaving the operating room the patient was extubated and with the help of the anesthesia personnel, the "glide scope" was inserted into the hypopharynx and the larynx and vocal cords visualized, showing symmetric movement of the cords. This was confirmed by multiple observers. The procedure was terminated. The patient tolerated the procedure well and she was taken to the recovery area in stable condition. Estimated blood loss was 80cc. Sponge and needle counts were correct times two.

What are the CPT® and ICD-9-CM codes reported?

Case 4

Preoperative diagnosis: Post-hemorrhagic hydrocephalus.

Postoperative diagnosis: Post-hemorrhagic hydrocephalus.

Operation: 1. Insertion of left frontal ventriculoperitoneal shunt.
                2. Removal of right frontal external ventricular drain.

Primary surgeon and Assistant Surgeon used.

Anesthesia: General endotracheal.

Operative indication: Patient is an 8-year-old boy who suffered a significant head trauma with intraventricular hemorrhage. He previously had an external ventricular drain placed. He failed clamp trial. Plan was made for permanent shunt implantation. The risks and benefits of surgery were discussed in detail with the patient and family. Risks include bleeding, infection, stroke, paralysis, seizure, coma, and death. All questions were answered in detail. I believe the patient and family understand the risks and benefits of surgery and wish to proceed.

Operative account: Patient was brought in the operating room and placed under general endotracheal anesthesia. His head was turned to the right, and a shoulder roll was placed. He was then clipped, prepped, and draped in the usual sterile fashion. Using the micro-point electrocautery, a half-moon incision was carried out over the patient's left coronal suture at the mid-pupillary line. The galea was divided and the scalp flap retracted. A 2nd incision was created above and behind the pinna of the ear.

Attention was turned to the abdomen where a 2 cm incision was carried out just to the left and superior to the umbilicus. Using the micropoint electrocautery, subcutaneous dissection was carried down to the superficial rectus fascia. The fascia was secured with hemostats, elevated, and opened sharply in a vertical fashion. This allowed dissection of the underlying muscular fibers. We secured then the deep rectus fascia with hemostats, elevated this, and opened this sharply. The underlying peritoneum was visible. This was secured and opened, allowing passage easily of a #4 Penfield into the peritoneal cavity.

A subcutaneous tunneler was then used to bring a Medtronic BioGlide catheter from the abdominal to the retroauricular incisions. This was then brought to the anterior incision. It was secured to the distal end of the Medtronic Delta valve, performance level 1, with 3-0 silk tie. The Midas perforator was then used to create a burr hole. The brain needle was then placed to the dura and electrocautery applied, creating a small durotomy, through which the brain needle was advanced. This was advanced into the ventricle with excellent return of cerebrospinal fluid under elevated pressure. We observed slightly stiff ependymal walls at the time of passage.

The brain needles were removed and a new Medtronic BioGlide ventricular catheter advanced down this track with excellent return of cerebrospinal fluid. This catheter was trimmed and secured to the proximal end of the valve with 3-0 silk suture. Spontaneous flow of cerebrospinal fluid was observed at the distal end of the peritoneal catheter prior to placement within the peritoneum. All wounds were then thoroughly irrigated with vancomycin-containing saline, and 1 mL of vancomycin-containing saline was injected into the bulb of the shunt.

At the 2 cranial incisions, the galea was reapproximated with inverted 3-0 Vicryl suture. Skin edges were approximated with a running 5-0 Monocryl stitch. At the abdominal incision, the peritoneum and deep rectus fascia were closed with a 3-0 Vicryl pursestring. Superficial rectus fascia was closed with interrupted 3-0 Vicryl suture. Subcutaneous tissue was reapproximated with interrupted and inverted 3-0 Vicryl suture. Skin edges were reapproximated with a running 5-0 Monocryl stitch. That wound was washed and dried, and a sterile dressing was applied. At the cranial wound, the patient's hair was shampooed and bacitracin ointment applied to the wounds. The patient was awakened, extubated, and taken to the recovery room in stable condition.

What are the CPT® and ICD-9-CM codes reported for the primary surgeon?

Case 5

Preoperative diagnosis: Acute epidural hematoma

Postoperative diagnosis: As above

Anesthetic agent: General Endotracheal

Operation: Left craniotomy for evacuation of epidural hematoma (emergent)

Indications: The patient presented with a history of a motor vehicle accident. He presented to the emergency room neurologically intact but while there became gradually less responsive and required intubation. An urgent CT scan revealed a large epidural hematoma and the patient was taken emergently to the operating room for evacuation.

Procedure/techniques/description of findings/condition of patient: The patient was brought to the operating room and after induction of adequate general anesthesia, prepped and draped in the usual sterile fashion for a left frontotemporal parietal craniotomy. A curvilinear incision was made beginning just anterior to the left ear curving posteriorly than upward and anteriorly to and at the hair line just off the midline. The resulting musculocutaneous flap was then reflected anteriorly. Multiple burr holes were then placed and connected using the high-speed drill to create a large free bone flap. This was removed from the immediate operative field. Directly beneath the bone flap was a large well-formed clots which delivered itself from the epidural space. A bleeding point was found in the region of the middle meningeal artery. This was carefully and thoroughly coagulated using bipolar correlation. A small opening was then made in the dura to ensure that there was not an underlying blood clot. There was not. This opening was primarily closed using 4-0 Nurolon. Additional meticulous hemostasis was then obtained. The bone flap was then replaced and held in place using multiple K LS fixation devices. Skin was then reapproximated using 2-0 Vicryl for the subcutaneous tissues and 5-0

Monocryl for the skin. The patient was then awakened from anesthesia at which time his vital signs were stable and he was neurologically improved from preoperatively.

Estimated blood loss: 100 cc

Specimens: None

Labs ordered: None

Diagnostic procedures ordered: None

Complications: None

> **What are the CPT® and ICD-9-CM codes?**

Case 6

Preoperative diagnoses: 1. Low back pain.
                          2. Degenerative lumbar disc.

Postoperative diagnoses: 1. Low back pain.
                           2. Degenerative lumbar disc.

Procedure performed: 1. Bilateral facet joint injection of steroid at the L4–L5 and L5–S1 with fluoroscopic guidance.

Description of procedure: The patient was transferred to the operative suite and placed in the prone position with a pillow under the abdomen. A smooth IV sedation was given with midazolam and fentanyl. The patient's back was prepped with Betadine in a sterile fashion, and we used lidocaine, 1% plain as a local anesthetic at the injection site. With the use of fluoroscopy assistance, first to the right and then to the left 20-degree, the scotty-dog view was identified, and we were able to place the spinal 22-gauge needle first to the right L4–L5, then right L5–S1, then to the left L4–L5, and then to left L5–S1. We used a lateral X-ray to assess the proper placement of the needle. We proceeded to inject a mixture of 4 mL of 0.25% Marcaine plain plus 80 mg of methylprednisolone and divided between the four joints. The needles were removed. The patient's back was cleaned, and a Band-Aid was applied. The patient was transferred to the recovery area with no apparent procedural complications.

> **What are the CPT® and ICD-9-CM codes?**

Case 7

Operation performed: Right-sided hemicraniectomy with duraplasty.

Complications: None.

Anesthesia: General endotracheal.

Estimated blood loss: Approximately 400 mL

Indications: is a 56-year-old male with significant past medical history who came in this evening with an ischemic infarct to his right MCA territory which converted to hemorrhagic transformation. The significant shift was following commands on the right side and hemiplegic on the left side. After a thorough discussion with the family, we explained to them that this would be a life saving procedure and we could not ensure that there would be any further neurological improvement from the state that he was in. They understood these risks and wanted to proceed ahead.

Operation performed: After informed consent was obtained, the patient was taken to the operating room and induced under general endotracheal anesthesia without incident. TEE monitor was placed due to the patients significant cardiac history; at this point, a roll was placed underneath the right shoulder and the head was placed in a horseshoe reverse question mark incision was taken through midline. This area was sterilely prepped and draped in usual fashion. A#10 blade was used to make an incision sharply. Raney clips were applied to the skin edges. The temporalis fascia and muscle was then resected with the cutaneous flap anteriorly. This was done until the keyhole could be identified. The musculocutaneous flap was then retracted with towel hooks, rubber bands and Allis clamps. The perforator was then used to make several burr holes approximately 6 and a footplate was then put on to perform the hemicraniectomy. We ensured that we were off midline to ensure that we did not get into the sagittal sinus or any draining veins associated with this. Once the bone was removed, hemostasis was obtained and the dura was opened in the C-shaped fashion. and a large piece of Durepair was placed underneath this. There was a small subdural which was also evacuated and a large piece of Durepair was then used to create a duraplasty. This was stitched in several points with 4.0 nylon. Hemovac was then tunneled through as well.

At this point the galea and the temporalis fascia was then reapproximated with 0 Vicryl interrupted fashion, overlying galea was reapproximated 0 Vicryl interrupted fashion. The overlying skin was closed with staples and the Hemovac drain was secured with 2-0 nylon. At the end of the case all counts of the needles and sponges were correct.

What are the CPT® and ICD-9-CM codes reported?

Case 8

Preoperative diagnosis: Dorsal column stimulator battery malfunction.

Postoperative diagnosis: Dorsal column stimulator battery malfunction.

Procedure performed: Replacement of dorsal column stimulator generator.

Attending: MD

Anesthesia: Monitored anesthetic coverage with local.

Estimated blood loss: Less than 5 mL

Specimens: None.

Drains: None.

Complications: None.

Implants: Medtronics prime advanced nonreconstructable generator.

Indications: This woman has a dorsal column stimulator in place and has benefited from the therapy. Her current device began malfunctioning approximately a month prior to this procedure and she has gradually noticed declining effectiveness. The device was interrogated approximately a week prior to this procedure and telemetry was obtainable, indicating a breakdown of the battery. On this basis, revision of the device was offered and accepted.

Procedure in brief: After extensive preoperative counseling, informed consent was obtained. The patient was brought to the operating room, positioned on the table in the left lateral decubitus position. Sedation was induced and a dose of antibiotics was administered IV. A wide area of the right lateral flank region surrounding her existing scar was prepped and draped in standard fashion and infiltrated with 0.5% Marcaine with 1:200,000 epinephrine. The skin was incised. The pouch housing the existing battery was entered. The battery was explanted, a new prime advanced generator was prepared. The leads were disconnected from the old generator and connected to the new generator in the same orientation. An impedance test was performed, which yielded acceptable results. The generator was implanted and secured to the fascia using 0 Ethibond suture. The wound was irrigated copiously and closed in layers using interrupted 0 and 3-0 Vicryl sutures followed by Mastisol and Steri-Strips to reapproximate the skin. Sterile dressing was applied. The patient was aroused from sedation and taken to recovery area in good condition. All final needle arid sponge counts were correct. There were no apparent complications.

What are the CPT® and ICD-9-CM codes reported?

Case 9

Preoperative diagnosis: Spinal stenosis at L4–L5

Postoperative diagnosis: Spinal stenosis at L4–L5

Operation performed: Right L4–L5 laminotomy, foraminotomy, decompression, bilateral decompression of the lateral recess

Operative anesthesia: General endotracheal tube anesthesia.

Estimated blood loss: Minimal.

Operative complications: None apparent.

Operative findings: Tight stenosis at L4–L5 from ligament hypertrophy and facet arthropathy.

Operative indications:
The patient is a 51-year-old gentleman. He has had ongoing lower extremity pain with numbness and tingling on the right hand side more so than the left side. He has had paresthesias. He has had progressive loss of strength. He has had very little back pain, however. The patient is brought to the operating room for operative decompression with an MRI scan that shows tight spinal stenosis at L4–L5, having failed conservative measures to date.

Description of procedure:
The patient was given 1 gm of Kefzol preoperatively. He was taken to the operating room where he underwent general endotracheal tube anesthesia without complications. All appropriate anesthetic monitors and lines were placed. He was placed prone onto a Wilson frame which was padded in the usual fashion. All pressure points were checked and padded appropriately. The patient's back was then outlined with a marking pen through the L4–L5 level in a vertical direction. He was then prepped using Prevail solution and allowed to dry. He was draped using sterile technique. Marcaine 0.25% with 1:200,000 units of epinephrine was instilled in the proposed incision for a total of 10 cc of injection. Using a #10 blade scalpel, a vertical midline incision was made. The soft tissues were dissected down to the thoracolumbar fascia using Bovie coagulation. The fascia was incised on the right hand side and the paraspinal muscles were stripped off the lamina and spinous processes of L4 and L5 on the right. A self-retaining Taylor retractor was placed into the wound and intraoperative fluoroscopy revealed the L4–L5 level. The soft tissue in the interlaminar space was then resected with a rongeur. The ligamentum flavum was resected with Kerrison punches and cervical curets. The laminotomy was performed on the superior aspect of L5 and the undersurface of L4. The laminotomy was taken out to the medial edge of the pedicle. A foraminotomy was performed with a #3 Kerrison punch for the exiting right L5 nerve root. The lateral recess was now decompressed. The disc was inspected and found not to be ruptured. We then performed a similar procedure on the left and the laminotomy was taken to the medial edge of the left pedicle. We then decompressed the patient's left side by slightly depressing the thecal sac with cottonoids and under-cutting the interspinous ligament with Kerrison punches so that the left lateral recess was also decompressed from overgrowth of the ligamentum flavum. The wound was copiously irrigated using warm bacitracin solution. Depo-Medrol 40 mg in 1 cc was placed epidurally. A piece of Gelfoam was placed over

the laminotomy defect to try to preserve the epidural space, and the wound was ready for closure. During all areas of closure, bacitracin irrigation was used in copious amounts. The fascia was closed with #0 Vicryl in an interrupted fashion. The subcutaneous tissue was closed with #30 Vicryl in an interrupted fashion. The skin was closed with #40 Vicryl in an interrupted fashion to the subcuticular space. Steri-Strips were placed on the wound. A sterile dressing was placed. The patient was taken to the recovery room in stable condition with sponge and needle counts correct times three.

What are the CPT® and ICD-9-CM codes?

Case 10

Preoperative diagnosis: Left L5 radiculopathy; left L5–S1 neural foraminal narrowing.

Postoperative diagnosis: Left L5 radiculopathy; left L5–S1 neural foraminal narrowing.

Procedure performed: Hemilaminectomy with left L5–S1 foraminotomy; microsurgical technique.

Anesthesia: General endotracheal.

Estimated blood loss: 25 mL.

Specimens: None.

Drains: None.

Complications: None.

Indications: This woman has a history of left lower extremity L5 radicular pain. She has had previous surgery in the lumbar region for a herniated disk. Her preoperative exam was remarkable for subjective complaints in an L5 pattern on the left. Her MRI scan showed high-grade neural foraminal narrowing on the left due to facet arthropathy. Based on these findings, treatment options were discussed including ongoing conservative therapy and surgical intervention. After contemplating alternatives, the patient elected to proceed with surgery.

Description of procedure: After extensive preoperative counseling, informed consent was obtained. The patient was brought to the operating room, intubated, placed under general anesthesia, and positioned in the prone position. A wide area of the lumbar region was prepped and draped in standard fashion. A midline incision was marked overlying the L5–S1 spinous processes and infiltrated with 0.5% Marcaine with 1:200,000 epinephrine, A standard surgical timeout was performed wherein the patient was identified and the surgical site and procedure were confirmed. Preop dose of antibiotics was administered IV. The skin was incised, subcutaneous bleeding points were controlled. The subcutaneous fat was transgressed to the lumbodorsal fascia, which was incised in the midline from the top of the spinous process of L5 through the bottom of the spinous process of S1. Paraspinous musculature was elevated subperiosteally and reflected laterally towards the patient's left. A high speed osteotome was used to create a trailing edge laminotomy of L5 and a leading edge laminotomy of S1, encompassing the medial 3rd of the facet complex. Microscope was then employed for magnification and illumination. A variety of curettes and rongeurs were then used to complete the laminotomy. The bone resection was carried laterally until the medial edge of the pedicle was encountered. As the bone resection and ligamentous resection was conducted, a large fragment of synovium type material with admixed scar tissue was extracted, resulting in marked decompression of the thecal sac and root sleeve. A probe could then be admitted through the neural foramen. For this aspect of the procedure, the microscope was utilized for magnification and illumination. A confirmatory X-ray was obtained with the probe inserted through the L5–S1 foramen, both the L5 and S1 root sleeves were directly visualized and were completely without impingement. Hemostasis was achieved with bipolar coagulation. A bulging of the disk was appreciated, but the decision was made to forego a diskectomy. A pledget of fat was harvested from the subcutaneous tissue and tucked in the laminotomy defect. A layered closure was then conducted using interrupted 0 Vicryl sutures. The lumbodorsal fascia was closed using interrupted 0 Vicryl sutures in watertight fashion. The skin was closed using interrupted buried subcuticular 3-0 Vicryl sutures followed by Mastisol and Steri-Strips. Sterile dressing was applied. The patient was aroused from anesthesia and extubated without difficulty. All final needle and sponge counts were correct. There were no perioperative complications.

What are the CPT® and ICD-9-CM codes reported?

Case 1

Anesthesia: Laryngeal mask anesthesia.

Preoperative diagnosis: Retinal detachment, right eye.

Postoperative diagnosis: Retinal detachment, right eye.

Procedure: Scleral buckle, cryoretinopexy, drainage of subretinal fluid, C3F8 gas in the right eye.

Procedure: After the patient had received adequate laryngeal mask anesthesia, he was prepped and draped in usual sterile fashion. A wire lid speculum was placed in the right eye.

A limbal peritomy was done for 360 degrees using 0.12 forceps and Westcott scissors. Each of the intramuscular quadrants was dissected using Aebli scissors. The muscles were isolated using a Gass muscle hook with an 0 silk suture attached to it. The patient had an inspection of the intramuscular quadrants and there was no evidence of any anomalous vortex veins or thin sclera. The patient had an examination of the retina using an indirect ophthalmoscope and he was noted to have 3 tears in the temporal and inferotemporal quadrant and 2 tears in the superior temporal quadrant. These were treated with cryoretinopexy. Most posterior edge of each of the tears was marked with a scleral marker followed by a surgical marking pen. The patient had 5-0 nylon sutures placed in each of the 4 intramuscular quadrants. The 2 temporal sutures were placed with the anterior bite at about the muscle insertion, the posterior bite 9 mm posterior to this. In the nasal quadrants the anterior bite was 3 mm posterior to the muscle insertion and the posterior bite was 3 mm posterior to this. A 240 band was placed 360 degrees around the eye and a 277 element from approximately the 5-1 o'clock position. The patient had another examination of the retina and was noted to have a moderate amount of subretinal fluid, so a drainage sclerotomy site was created at approximately the 9:30 o'clock position incising the sclera until the choroid was visible. The choroid was then punctured with a #30-gauge needle. A moderate amount of subretinal fluid was drained from the subretinal space. The eye became relatively soft and 0.35 ml of C3FS gas was injected into the vitreous cavity 3.5 mm posterior to the limbus. The superior temporal and inferior temporal and superior nasal sutures were tied down over the scleral buckle. The 240 band was tightened up and excessive scleral buckling material was removed from the eye. The inferior nasal suture was tied down over the scleral buckle and all knots were rotated posteriorly. The eye was reexamined. The optic nerve was noted to be nicely perfused. The tears were supported on the scleral buckle. There was a small amount of residual subretinal fluid. The patient received posterior sub-Tenon Marcaine for postoperative pain control. The 0 silk sutures were removed from the eye. The conjunctiva was closed with #6-0 plain gut suture. The patient received subconjunctival Ancef and dexamethasone. The patient was patched with atropine and Maxitrol ointment.

The patient tolerated the procedure well and returned to the postoperative recovery room.

What are the CPT® and ICD-9-CM codes?

Case 2

Preoperative diagnosis: Dacryostenosis, both eyes.

Postoperative diagnosis: Dacryostenosis, both eyes.

Procedure performed: Nasolacrimal duct probing, both eyes.

Anesthesia: General.

Condition: To recovery, satisfactory.

Counts: Needle count correct.

Estimated blood loss: Less than 1 mL.

Informed consent: The procedure, risks, benefits, and alternatives were thoroughly explained to the patient's parent who understands and wants the procedure done.

Procedure: The patient was prepped and draped in the usual sterile manner under general anesthesia. Starting on the right eye the upper punctum was dilated with double-ended punctal dilator, and starting with a 4-0 probe, increasing up to a 2-0 probe, the nasolacrimal duct was probed patent. Then using a curved 23- gauge punctal irrigator 0.125 ml of sterile fluorescein stained saline was easily irrigated down the nasolacrimal duct into the nostril where it was carefully collected with a clear #8 catheter. Then instruments were removed and an identical procedure was done on the opposite eye nasolacrimal duct. TobraDex eye drops were placed in each lower cul-de-sac. The eyelids were closed. The patient left the operating room for recovery in satisfactory condition.

What are the CPT® and ICD-9-CM codes reported?

Case 3

Preoperative diagnosis: Bilateral protruding ears.

Postoperative diagnosis: Bilateral protruding ears.

Procedure: Bilateral otoplasty.

Anesthesia: General.

Estimated blood loss: Minimal.

Complications: None.

Procedure is as follows: The patient was placed in the supine position. She was prepped and draped in the usual sterile fashion. Measurements were taken from the helix to the mastoid at the superior, mid, and inferior portions and they were within 1 to 2 mm of the same bilaterally and were approximately 17 mm superior, 24 mm middle, and 25 mm inferior. The right ear was begun first. A curved incision was made just anterior to the sulcus of the posterior ear. This was done with a 15-blade scalpel. Electrocautery was used for hemostasis and further dissection. An iris scissors was used to dissect the soft tissues off of the mastoid region and the posterior ear. The concha was shut back and sutured in place with clear 4-0 nylon suture and in a horizontal mattress pattern. Three tacking sutures were used. This brought the ear back approximately 2 to 3 mm. However, greater correction was needed and, therefore, Mustarde' sutures were placed.

The mid and superior portions of the antihelical fold were placed. These were spaced widely on either side of the helical fold. They were then sutured in place, tacking the fold more acutely to a point that was deemed acceptable and held in that position. So in this, a margin of skin was excised along the posterior ear and closure of the wound was performed with 5-0 chromic suture. Prior to closure, full hemostasis had been obtained with electrocautery. Both ears were done in the exact same fashion; therefore, only one is dictated in detail.

The patient was then checked very carefully for symmetry. Postoperative measurements were approximately 14 mm superior, 15 mm mid, and 16 mm lower.

What are the CPT® and ICD-9-CM codes reported?

Case 4

Preoperative diagnosis: Right otosclerosis.

Postoperative diagnosis: Right otosclerosis.

Type of procedure: Right stapedectomy.

Anesthesia: General endotracheal.

Findings: There was otosclerosis on the anterior footplate of the stapes with preoperative conductive hearing loss in the right ear.

Description of procedure: The patient was taken to the OR and placed in the supine position. Following induction of general endotracheal anesthesia, the head was turned to the left and the right ear was prepped and draped in the usual fashion. Then 1% Xylocaine with 1:100,000 epinephrine was infiltrated in the skin along the posterior ear canal wall and the skin over the tragus.

After a short waiting time, an incision was made over the tragus, and a piece of posterior tragal perichondrium was harvested for a graft and set aside to dry. A speculum was then placed in the canal. The canal was quite large. An incision was made along the posterior canal wall, and a tympanomeatal flap was elevated and laid forward to include the fibrous annulus without perforation. The middle ear was inspected. The ossicular chain was palpated, and otosclerosis appeared to be fixing the stapes. The chorda tympani nerve was very carefully preserved and not manipulated and was kept moist throughout the procedure. No curetting of bone was necessary in order to access the footplate. A control hole was made in the footplate with a straight pick. The incudostapedial joint was separate with an IS joint knife. The stapedius tendon was severed, and the superstructure of the stapes was fractured over the promontory and removed. The footplate was then picked out with a 45-degree pick, completely removing all fragments. Great care was taken not to suction in the vestibule. The distance between the incus and the oval window was then measured. The tragal perichondrial graft was then taken and laid over the oval window with complete coverage. A 3.75 Shea platinum Teflon cup piston was then chosen. The platinum wires were opened and the shaft was placed down against the graft and into the oval window niche. The cup was placed under the long process of the incus by gently lifting the incus, and the platinum wires were snugly crimped around the long process of the incus. An excellent round window reflex was achieved upon palpation of the ossicular chain at this point.

Small dry pressed Gelfoam pledgets were then placed around the shaft of the prosthesis and over the graft. The tympanomeatal flap was replaced. The lateral surface of the drum was covered with Gelfoam, and the canal was filled with antibiotic ointment. The incision over the tragus was closed with running, interlocking 5-0 plain, fast-absorbing gut. A cotton ball was placed in the canal, and the patient was awakened, extubated, and returned to recovery in satisfactory condition. He will be discharged when fully awake and will return to my office in two weeks. He will avoid strenuous activity, keep the ear dry, keep a clean cotton ball in the ear, apply antibiotic ointment to the tragal incision, avoid driving while dizzy, and he was given prescriptions for Lorcet Plus, Keflex, and Xanax.

What are the CPT® and ICD-9-CM codes reported?

Case 5

Preoperative Diagnosis: Serous otitis media with effusion and adenoidal hypertrophy.

Postoperative Diagnosis: Serous otitis media with effusion, and adenoidal hypertrophy.

Name of Procedure: Bilateral ventilation tube placement, Donaldson-Activent type, Adenoidectomy.

Anesthesia: General

Estimated Blood Loss: Less than 5 mL.

Findings: Patient s a 1 ½ -year-old white male with a history of the above noted diagnosis. Operative findings included bilateral thickened drums. He had a right serous effusion. The left was aerated for the most part. He had an intact palate and a 3-4 + adenoid pad.

Technique: Patient was brought into the operative suite and comfortably positioned on the table. General mask anesthesia was induced. Appropriate drapes were placed. Attention was turned to the right ear. The external canal was cleaned of cerumen and irrigated with alcohol. A radial incision was made in the right tympanic membrane. Middle ear was evacuated of effusion and Donaldson-Activent tube was followed by Ciprodex otic drops. The same procedure was performed on the contralateral side. The bed was turned 30° m clockwise fashion. The Crowe-Davis mouth gag was inserted and suspended. The palate was palpated and felt to be intact. The soft palate was elevated and under direct nasopharyngoscopy the adenoid was removed with powered adenoidectomy blade taking care to avoid injury to the eustachian tube orifice. The base was cauterized with Bovie suction cautery and a pack was placed. After several minutes the packs were removed. The nasopharynx and oral cavity was irrigated and suctioned free of debris. The stomach was evacuated with orogastric tube. Reevaluation showed no further active bleeding. Further drapes and instruments were removed. The patient was returned to the care of Anesthesia, allowed to awaken, extubated and transported in stable condition to the recovery room having tolerated the procedure well.

What are the CPT® and ICD-9-CM codes reported?

Case 6

Preoperative diagnosis:
Tympanic membrane perforation, conductive hearing loss in the right ear.

Postoperative diagnosis: Tympanic membrane perforation, conductive hearing loss in the right ear.

Name of procedure: Right tympanoplasty via the postauricular approach.

Anesthesia: General.

Estimated blood loss: Less than 20 ml.

Complications: None.

Specimens: None.

Indications: This is a 9-year-old white female with the above diagnoses and now presents for surgical intervention.

Intraoperative findings: Intraoperative findings revealed tympanosclerosis posteriorly with a central eardrum perforation of approximately 30% of the surface of the eardrum. There was no cholesteatoma. The ossicular chain is intact.

Description of operattve procedure: Under satisfactory general anesthesia the patient was given preoperative intravenous antibiotic. The right ear was prepared and draped in the usual sterile fashion. A postauricular incision was made and the temporalis fascia graft was harvested. The posterior ear canal skin was elevated and tympanomeatal flap was developed. The Rosen needle was used to freshen the edge of the perforation. Gelfoam was placed in the middle ear space. The graft was cut into the appropriate size and laid medial to the remnant of the tympanic membrane anteriorly, posteriorly, inferiorly and superiorly. Antibiotic ointment and Gelfoam were placed in the ear canal. Closure of the wound was done in layers with 4-0 Vicryl for the subcutaneous tissue and 4-0 Prolene for skin. Pressure dressing was placed around the right ear. The patient tolerated the procedure well.

What are the CPT® and ICD-9-CM codes reported?

Case 7

Operative Report

Preoperative diagnosis:
Foreign body, right external ear canal.

Anesthetic: General. TIME BEGAN: 1015 TIME ENDED: 1035

Postoperative diagnosis: Foreign body, right external ear canal.

Pathology Specimen: None.

Operation: Removal of foreign body using the microscope.

Date of procedure: 05/12/xx TIME BEGAN: 1021 TIME ENDED: 1022

Description of operation:
Under general anesthesia with the microscope in place, a pearly white plastic ball was seen virtually obstructing the entire ear canal. Gently with a curette, this was teased out of the ear canal atraumatically. The ear canal and eardrum were perfectly intact.

The patient tolerated the procedure well and was returned to the recovery room in satisfactory condition.

What are the CPT® and ICD-9-CM codes reported?

Case 8

Preoperative diagnosis: Left lower eyelid basal cell carcinoma

Postoperative diagnosis: Left lower eyelid basal cell carcinoma

Operation: Excision of left lower eyelid basal cell carcinoma with flaps and full thickness skin graft and tarsorrhaphy.

Indication for surgery: The patient is a very pleasant female who complains of a one year history of a left lower eyelid lesion and this was recently biopsied and found to be basal cell carcinoma. She was advised that she would benefit from a complete excision of the left lower eyelid lesion. She is aware of the risks of residual tumor, infection, bleeding, scarring and possible need for further surgery. All questions have been answered prior to the day of surgery. She consents to the surgery.

Operative procedure:
The patient was placed on the operating room table in the supine position and an intravenous line was established by hospital staff prior to sedation and analgesia. Throughout the entire case the patient received monitored anesthesia care. The patient's entire face was prepped and draped in the usual sterile fashion with a Betadine solution and topical tetracaine and corneal protective shields were placed over both corneas. A surgical marking pen was used to mark the tumor. 3 mm markings were obtained around the tumor. The tumor was noted to encompass approximately 1/3 of the left lower eyelid. A wedge resection was performed and this was marked and 2% Xylocaine with 1:100,000 epinephrine, 0.5% Marcaine with 1:100,000 epinephrine was infiltrated around the lesion. This was excised with a #15 blade. This was sent for intraoperative fresh frozen sections. Intraoperative fresh frozen sections revealed persistent basal cell carcinoma at the medial margin. Another 2 mm of margin was discarded and a revised left lower eyelid medial margin was sent for permanent sections. The area could not be closed primarily thus a tarsoconjunctival advancement flap was advanced from the left upper eyelid to fill the defect. This was sutured in place with multiple 5-0 Vicryl sutures. The anterior lamella defect of skin was closed by harvesting a full-thickness skin graft from the left upper eyelid and placing it in the left lower eyelid defect. This was sutured in place with multiple interrupted 5-0 chromic gut sutures. The eyelids were sutured shut both on the medial aspect of the Hughes flap as well as the lateral aspect of the Hughes flap with a 4-0 silk suture. A pressure dressing and TobraDex ointment were applied. The patient tolerated the procedure well and was transported back to the recovery area in excellent condition.

What are the CPT® and ICD-9-CM codes reported?

Case 9

Preoperative diagnosis:

1. Phacomorphic cataract, right eye.

Postoperative diagnosis:

Cataract, right eye.

Procedure:

1. Complex phacoemulsification with manual stretch of the iris, right eye.
2. Peripheral iridectomy, right eye.

Anesthesia: Topical.

Indications: The patient was seen in the Ophthalmology office with a complaint of decreased vision in the right eye and was diagnosed with a cataract, right eye. The patient was symptomatic and therefore given the option of cataract surgery for improved vision or observation. The details of the procedure were discussed at length as well as the potential risks which include but are not limited to permanent decrease of vision from infection, inflammation, bleeding, retinal detachment and need for reoperation. The patient understood the above and desired to proceed with cataract surgery.

Description of procedure: The patient received dilating drops and anesthesia in the preoperative area and was later brought into the operating room. The patient was sedated by the anesthesia staff. The patient was then prepped and draped in the usual sterile manner. The microscope was focused onto the right eye and the speculum was inserted to separate the eyelids. The tip of the 2.8 mm keratome blade was used at the 6:00 o'clock position to create the paracentesis that after which Amvisc plus was injected into the anterior chamber to create a deep anterior chamber. The same blade was used at 1:00 o'clock to create the main clear corneal wound into the anterior chamber. A two hand technique using iris expansion devices was used to expand the size of the pupil. The instruments were used at the sites directly opposite of one another to stretch the iris. They were then rotated 180 degrees to stretch the iris in that new meridian. The cystotome needle on the balanced salt solution syringe was used to initially create the capsulorrhexis flap and the capsulorrhexis forceps were used to create the continuous capsulorrhexis tear. A flat tip hydrodissection cannula on the balanced salt solution syringe was used to hydrodissect and hydrodelineate the lens. The phacoemulsification unit was used to remove the nucleus and irrigation and aspiration was used to remove the residual cortex. The bag was inflated with Amvisc plus and a lens of 27.5 diopter model SI40MB was injected into the bag and then dialed into place. The Amvisc plus was removed with irrigation and aspiration mode. The anterior chamber was then inflated to the appropriate firmness using balanced salt solution. After the globe was inflated to the appropriate firmness, 0.1 cc of Vancomycin was injected into the anterior chamber. The wounds were checked for leakage and none was found. The globe was checked for appropriate firmness and found to be desirable. The speculum was disinserted and the patient was brought into the postoperative area where postoperative instructions for surgical eye care were given, including the use of topical eye drops and the need for subsequent follow up.

What are the CPT® and ICD-9-CM codes reported?

Case 10

IV Sedation and Local

Preoperative diagnosis: Cataract of the Left Eye

Postoperative diagnosis: Cataract of the Left Eye

Procedure performed: Cataract Extraction, Foldable Posterior Chamber Intraocular Lens of the Left Eye

Procedure: The patient was brought to the Operating Room and placed on the operating table in the supine position. An intravenous line was started in the patient's left arm. After appropriate sedation, a left O'Brien and left retrobulbar block were administered, which consisted of a 50/60 mixture of 0.75% Bupivacaine and 2% lidocaine. The Honan balloon was then placed over the operative eye. While the surgeon scrubbed for 5 minutes the patient was prepped and draped in the usual sterile fashion including instillation of 5% Betadine solution to the left cornea and cul-de-sac, which was irrigated with balanced salt solution and the use an eyelid drape. A limbal incision was performed with the super sharp blade. Provisc was injected into the anterior chamber. A capsulotomy was performed with a cystitome and Utrata forceps such that it was 6 mm and oval in shape. Hydrodissection was performed with balanced salt solution. The nucleus was removed using the phacoemulsification mode of the Alcon 20,000 Legacy Series System by divide and conquer technique under Viscoat control. The cortex was removed using the irrigation aspiration mode. The anterior chamber was then filled with Proviso and the AcrySof foldable posterior chamber intraocular lens was then inserted into the capsular bag and rotated into position such that the optic was well centered. The Proviso was removed using the irrigation and aspiration mode. Miochol was injected to constrict the pupil. The wound was checked and deemed to be watertight. A collagen shield soaked in Ciloxan and Pred Forte was applied. The standard postoperative patch and shield were placed and the patient was transferred to the Recovery Room in stable condition.

What are the CPT® and ICD-9-CM codes reported?

Case 1

CRNA performed anesthesia

Anesthesiologist medically directing two cases

Anesthesia Time: 9:30 to 10:06

Physical Status 3

Preoperative diagnosis: Cyst on knee

Postoperative diagnosis: Baker's Cyst

Procedure: Excision of Baker's Cyst, knee

Anesthesia: Monitored Anesthesia Care

What are the CPT® and ICD-9-CM Codes reported for the Anesthesiologist?

27345,

What are the CPT® and ICD-9-CM Codes reported for the CRNA?

What is the time reported for this service?

Case 2

Anesthesiologist personally performed

Anesthesia Time: 7:12 to 10:08

Physical Status 2

Preoperative diagnosis: Suspected Prostate Cancer

Postoperative diagnosis: Prostate Carcinoma

Procedure: Radical Retropubic Prostatectomy

Anesthesia: General

What are the CPT® and ICD-9-CM Codes reported for the Anesthesiologist?

00865-P2

185

What is the time reported for this service?

186

Case 3

Non-medically directed CRNA performed anesthesia and documented intra-operative placement of continuous femoral nerve catheter for post operative pain.

Anesthesia Time: 7:18 to 9:10

Physical Status 3

Preoperative diagnosis: Left Knee Osteoarthosis

Postoperative diagnosis: Left Knee Osteoarthrosis, localized primary, Acute post-operative pain

Procedure: Total knee arthroplasty

Anesthesia: General anesthesia provided for surgery, Surgeon requested post-operative pain management via continuous femoral catheter

What are the CPT® and ICD-9-CM Codes reported for the CRNA?

What is the time reported for this service?

00630 – AA – 33

724

Case 4

Anesthesia Start: 14:07 Anesthesia End: 17:33

Physical Status 3 Anesthesiologist: Michael D, MD

Operative Report

Preoperative diagnosis: Lumbar spinal stenosis

Postoperative diagnosis: L4–L5 spinal stenosis

Procedure:

L4–L5 laminectomy, removal of synovial cyst, bilateral medial facetectomy and posterolateral fusion L4–L5 with vertebral autograft, bone morphogenic protein, chip allograft, all with intraoperative somatosensory evoked potentials, electromyographies and loupe magnification.

Anesthesia: General endotracheal anesthesia.

Description of Procedure:

The patient was taken to the operating room and underwent intravenous anesthetic and orotracheal intubation. Her head was placed in the three-pin Mayfield headrest. She was turned into the prone position on a four-poster frame. All pressure points were carefully padded. The fluoroscope was brought in and sterilely draped to help localize the incision.

A midline incision was made between L4 and L5 through skin and subcutaneous tissue and the paraspinal muscles were dissected free of the spinous process, lamina, facets and L4, L5 transverse processes. Self-retainers were placed more deeply. We proceeded to use the double-action rongeur to remove the L4–L5 spinous process lamina. 3 and 4 millimeter Kerrison punches were used to complete the laminectomy including removing the hypertrophied ligamentum flavum. We made sure that we decompressed from the top of the L4 pedicle to the bottom of the L5 pedicle, which was confirmed with intraoperative fluoroscopy. The medial facets were drilled and then we undercut over the nerve roots with a 3 millimeter Kerrison punch. Hemostasis was achieved with powdered Gelfoam. We irrigated the wound. We decorticated the L4 and L5 transverse processes. We placed our vertebral autograft, bone morphogenic protein and chip allograft in the posterolateral gutters. Hemovac drain was placed. We closed the muscle with 0 Vicryl. Fascia was closed with 0 Vicryl. Subcutaneous tissue was closed with 2-0 Vicryl and the skin was closed with staples.

What are the CPT® and ICD-9-CM Codes reported for the Anesthesiologist?

What is the time reported for this service?

Case 5

CRNA directly supervised by anesthesiologist who is directing two other cases.

CRNA inserted Swan-Ganz catheter, a separate CVP, and an A-line

Patient has a severe systemic disease that is a constant threat to life

Anesthesia Time: 11:43 to 15:26

Preoperative diagnosis: Multivessel coronary artery disease.

Postoperative diagnosis: Coronary artery disease, native artery

Name of procedure: Coronary artery bypass graft x 3, left internal mammary artery to the LAD, saphenous vein graft to the obtuse marginal, saphenous vein graft to the diagonal.

Anesthesia: General

Brief history: This 77-year-old patient who was found to have a huge aneurysm. Preoperative cardiac clearance revealed a markedly positive stress test and cardiac catheterization showed critical left-sided disease. Coronary revascularization was recommended. The patient has multiple medical illnesses including chronic obstructive pulmonary disease with emphysema and chronic renal insufficiency. I discussed with the patient and the family, the risks of operation including the risk of bleeding, infection, stroke, blood transfusion, renal failure, and death. At operation, we harvested a vein from the left leg using an endoscopic technique that turned out to be a very good conduit. Her obtuse marginal vessel was a 1.5 mm diffusely diseased vessel that was bypassed distally as it ran in the left ventricular muscle. The diagonal was a surprisingly good vessel at 1.5 mm in size. The LAD was bypassed in the mid aspect of the LAD and there was distal disease though a 1.5 mm probe passed quite easily. Good flow was measured in the graft. The patient came off bypass very nicely. Note should be made that her ascending aorta was calcified and we used a single clamp technique.

Description of Operative Procedure: Following delivery of the patient to the operating room, the patient was placed under general anesthetic, was prepped and draped in the usual sterile manner. Arterial line, Right Pulmonary Artery Catheter and a Left Subclavian central lines were placed by the Anesthesia Department. A median sternotomy was made and the left internal mammary artery was harvested from the left chest wall, the saphenous vein was harvested from the left leg. The patient was heparinized and cannulated and placed on cardiopulmonary bypass with an aortic cannula on the undersurface of the aortic arch and a venous cannula through the right atrial sidewall. Note should be made that the upper aorta was very heavily calcified, but the area that we cannulated was felt to be disease free. The aorta was cross clamped and the heart was stopped with antegrade and retrograde cardioplegic solution. The heart was retracted out of the pericardial sac and then displaced into the right chest which afforded good access to the lone marginal vessel which was bypassed with a reversed saphenous vein graft using a running 7-0 Prolene suture. Cold cardioplegic solution was then instilled down this graft. Note should be made that during the mammary artery harvest, the left lung was completely adherent to the left chest wall, most likely from old episodes of pneumonia.

Next, a second saphenous vein segment was placed to the diagonal vessel and then the left internal mammary artery was placed to the mid LAD. As noted, there was diffuse calcification distally in this artery just beyond the anastomosis, but the 1.5 mm probe passed very nicely and we felt that it was not necessary to double jump this LAD. With the cross clamp in place, two proximal aortotomies were made and the two proximal anastomoses were formed using 6-0 Prolene in a running fashion. Just prior to completion of the second anastomosis, appropriate de-airing maneuvers were performed and then the suture lines were tied as the cross clamp was removed. The patient was allowed to rewarm completely and was weaned from bypass. The cannulas were removed and the cannulation sites were secured with pursestring sutures. Once hemostasis was secured, chest tubes were placed and the wound was closed. Final needle, instrument, and sponge counts were reported as correct. The patient tolerated the procedure well and returned to the recovery room in stable condition.

What are the CPT® and ICD-9-CM Codes reported for the Anesthesiologist?

What are the CPT® and ICD-9-CM Codes reported for the CRNA?

What is the time reported for this service?

Case 6

CRNA performed anesthesia under medical direction of anesthesiologist

Anesthesiologist medically directing three cases

Anesthesia time: 8:52 to 9:34

Physical status 1

Preoperative diagnosis: Phimosis, congenital

Postoperative diagnosis: Phimosis, congenital

Procedure: Circumcision on six-month-old boy

Anesthesia: Monitored anesthesia care

What are the CPT® and ICD-9-CM Codes reported for the Anesthesiologist?

What are the CPT® and ICD-9-CM Codes reported for the CRNA?

What is the time reported for this service?

Case 7

CRNA performed anesthesia under medical direction of anesthesiologist

Anesthesiologist medically directing one case

CRNA placed arterial line

Anesthesia Time: 10:43 to 12:50

Physical Status 3

Preoperative Diagnosis: Left Renal Mass

Postoperative Diagnosis: Same

Procedure: Left Partial Nephrectomy, Laparoscopic

Anesthesia: General

Procedure Description: Abdominal wall insufflated. The laparoscope was placed through the umbilical port and additional trocars were placed into the abdominal cavity. Using the fiberoptic camera, the renal mass was identified and the diseased kidney tissue was removed using electrocautery. Minimal bleeding is noted. Instruments were removed and the abdominal incisions were closed by suture. Patient tolerated surgery well and was transferred to the Post Anesthesia Care Unit in satisfactory condition.

What are the CPT® and ICD-9-CM Codes reported for the Anesthesiologist?

What are the CPT® and ICD-9-CM Codes reported for the CRNA?

What is the time reported for this service?

Case 8

Anesthesiologist personally performed case

Anesthesia time: 13:04 to 13:41

Physical status 3

Preoperative diagnosis: RLL Lung Cavity, possible CA of lung

Postoperative diagnosis: Right Lower Lobe Lung Carcinoma

Procedure: Bronchoscopy

Anesthesia: Monitored anesthesia care

Procedure description: With the patient under satisfactory anesthesia, a flexible fiber-optic bronchoscope was introduced via oral cavity and advanced past the larynx for visualization of the bronchus. Cell washings were obtained and sent to pathology. The bronchoscope was then removed. Patient tolerated procedure well.

Cell washings obtained from the right lower lobe were confirmed by pathology as malignant carcinoma.

What are the CPT® and ICD-9-CM Codes reported for the Anesthesiologist?

What is the time reported for this service?

Case 9

Anesthesia services personally provided by Anesthesiologist

Physical Status 2

Anesthesia Start: 10:03—Anesthesia Stop: 11:06

Preoperative diagnosis: Sternal wound hematoma.

Postoperative diagnosis: Complicated upper abdominal wall wound.

Name of procedure: Sternal wound exploration and wound vac placement.

Anesthesia: Monitored Anesthesia Care

Brief history: He is a 52-year-old patient who is two weeks out from re-do sternotomy and aortic valve replacement for critical aortic stenosis in the setting of heart failure. He had a postoperative coagulopathy and required sternal re-exploration with open packing. He was closed the next day. He had serous discharged prior to going home but this was culture negative and the wound looked very good. He continued to have serous discharge in the clinic and it was felt he had a retained hematoma. He was scheduled for evaluation of the hematoma and wound vac placement. This was done without incident. He did not have any evidence of infection. There was no evidence of any sternal instability.

Description of operative procedure: Following delivery of the patient to the operating room, the patient was placed on the operating table, prepared and draped in the usual sterile manner. His upper abdominal wound was explored. There was hematoma at the base of the wound which was very carefully evacuated and the wound was irrigated with antibacterial solution. A wound vac was then placed with the assistance of the wound care nurse. The patient was returned to the PCU in stable condition.

What are the CPT® and ICD-9-CM Codes reported for the Anesthesiologist?

What is the time reported for this service?

Case 10

Anesthesia start: 12:18

Anesthesia end: 13:31

CRNA: John Sleep, CRNA (Non-Medically Directed)

ASA Physical status-III

Operative Report

Preoperative diagnosis: Stricture of the left ureter, postoperative

Postoperative diagnosis: SAME

Procedure:

1. Cystoscopy of ileal conduit.

2. Exchange of left nephroureteral catheter.

Anesthesia: Monitored anesthesia care.

Description of procedure: The patient is identified in the holding area, marked, taken to the operating room. Subsequently, she was given monitored anesthesia care. She was prepped and draped in the usual sterile fashion in the supine position. Next, using a flexible cystoscope, the ileal conduit was entered. Cystoscopy was performed, which showed the ureteroileal anastomosis on the left with a stent protruding from it. There were no calcifications seen on the stent. Thus, the cystoscope was removed from the ileal conduit and then a super stiff wire was advanced through the nephroureteral catheter, up into the kidney. Once it was up there, then the catheter was taken off of the wire and then a new 8-French x 28-centimeter, nephroureteral ureteral catheter was advanced fluoroscopically into the level of the kidney. Once this was done and its position was confirmed fluoroscopically, the wire was pulled. A good curl was there fluoroscopically in the kidney, as the wire was pulled. A good curl was seen in the bladder and then the distal end was protruding out from the ileal conduit. This was placed in the ostomy bag and the patient was taken in stable condition to the recovery room.

What are the CPT® and ICD-9-CM Codes reported for the CRNA?

What is the time reported for this service?

Case 1

Location: Regional Hospital

CT thorax w/contrast, CT abdomen w/contrast, CT pelvis w/contrast, low osmolar contrast

Exam: CT chest with contrast; CT abdomen with contrast; CT pelvis with contrast August 5, 20XX.

Comparison: CT chest Regional Hospital 7/8/20XX.

History: Non-small-cell lung cancer.

Technique: Axial images of the chest, abdomen pelvis with oral and 125 cc Omnipaque-300 intravenous contrast.

Findings: Chest CT shows left upper lobe and pulmonary mass which appear centrally necrotic abutting the posterior pleural surface and mediastinum without definitive invasion, 83 x 64 mm, prior 76 x 56 mm, image 15. Stable lingular and left basilar, right middle lobe and right lower lobe superior segment pleural-parenchymal opacity suggesting scarring. New mild subsegmental infiltrate left upper lobe. No pneumothorax or pleural fluid. No thoracic adenopathy. Heart size normal, no pericardial effusion. Left coronary arteriosclerotic calcification present. No osseous neoplasm. Abdomen CT shows normal liver, gallbladder, biliary ducts, pancreas, spleen, adrenal glands and kidneys. Stomach and duodenum within normal limits. Aortoiliac arterial sclerosis without aneurysm. No retroperitoneal adenopathy. Pelvis CT shows no mass, adenopathy or ascites. No bowel obstruction. No hernia. No osseous neoplasm. Lumbar spine degenerative change present. Left-sided muscle atrophy and brace noted.

Conclusion: 1. Increasing size left upper lobe pulmonary mass with central cavitation suggested. 2. No thoracic adenopathy or distant metastatic disease demonstrated. 3. Coronary arteriosclerosis.

What are the CPT® and ICD-9-CM codes reported?

Case 2

Location: Independent Diagnostic Testing Facility, radiologist employed by the facility.

CT brain/head w/wo contrast exam: CT head, without and with contrast August 5, 20XX

Comparison: None available.

History: Non-small-cell lung cancer.

Technique: Axial images of the calvarium without and with 125 cc Omnipaque-300 intravenous contrast.

Findings: The calvarium is intact. Imaged upper portions of the maxillary antra show minimal mucosal thickening. The sphenoid ethmoid and frontal sinuses are clear bilaterally. No hydrocephalus, mass effect, brain shift, abnormal extra-axial fluid collection or mass. Calcification left basal ganglia without mass effect, nonspecific, likely benign. Abnormal but nonspecific decreased density in the periventricular and subcortical white matter of the cerebral hemispheres bilaterally without mass effect or enhancement, most consistent with remote microvascular ischemic change present to mild degree. Bilateral intracavernous carotid and vertebral arteriosclerotic calcification. Probable anterior communicating artery aneurysm 6 x 5 mm. Recommend intracranial CT angiography to further characterize.

Conclusion: 1. No finding suggestive of metastatic disease. 2. Probable 6 x 5 mm anterior communicating artery aneurysm. Recommend intracranial CT angiography to further characterize. 3. Cerebrovascular arteriosclerosis. 4. Nonspecific cerebral white matter lesions most consistent with remote microvascular ischemic change. 5. Calcification left basal ganglia, likely benign; however, recommend continued imaging follow up.

What are the CPT® and ICD-9-CM codes reported?

Case 3

Location: Imaging center; radiologist employed.

Study: Mammogram bilateral screening, all views, producing direct digital image

Reason: Screen

Bilateral digital mammography with computer-aided detection (CAD)

No previous mammograms are available for comparison.

Clinical history: The patient has a positive family history of breast cancer.

Mammogram was read with the assistance of GE iCAD (computerized diagnostic) system.

Findings: Residual fibroglandular breast parenchymal tissue is identified bilaterally. No dominant spiculated mass or suspicious area of clustered pleomorphic microcalcifications are apparent. Skin and nipples are seen to be normal. The axilla are unremarkable.

Impression: BIRADS 1—Negative

What are the CPT® and ICD-9-CM codes reported?

Case 4

Location: Imaging center, radiologist employed.

Study: Femur AP and Lateral

Reason: Left leg pain

Left Femur:

Comparison: There are no prior studies for comparison.

Findings: There is no fracture or dislocation of the left femur. The femoral head is concentrically seated within the acetabulum without deformity of the femoral head.

Impression: Normal views of the left femur.

What are the CPT® and ICD-9-CM codes reported?

Case 5

Location: Regional hospital.

Study: Ultrasound Urinary Tract

Indications: Status ureteral reimplantation to evaluate for continued vesicoureteral reflux.

Left Kidney: Length: 7.0 cm
              Prior length: 7.4 cm
              Parenchyma: Cortical scarring.
              Pelvic dilatation: Normal
              Calyceal dilatation: Normal
              Hydronephrosis grade: Normal

Right Kidney: Length: 6.6 cm,
              Prior length: 6.4 cm,
              Parenchyma: Cortical scarring.
              Pelvic dilatation: Normal
              Calyceal dilatation: Normal
              Hydronephrosis grade: Normal
              Interval hydronephrosis change: None

Ureters: Normal.

Bladder: Almost empty and difficult to evaluate.

Impression:

1. Interval right renal enlargement without hydronephrosis.
2. Stable asymmetric small left renal size likely to represent diffuse cortical scarring.

What are the CPT® and ICD-9-CM codes reported for this service?

Case 6

Location: Regional Hospital

Examination:

1. CT enteroclysis (fluoro enteroclysis with CT abdomen—neutral enteral with iv contrast—2D reformats)
2. CT enteroclysis (fluoro enteroclysis with CT pelvis—neutral enteral with IV contrast—2D reformats)

Clinical indication: Unexplained abdominal pain and diarrhea, as well as weight loss. Normal colonoscopy.

Comparison: None.

Procedure: In accordance with policy and procedure standard medication reconciliation was performed by the radiologic technologist prior to IV contrast administration. No contraindication was identified.

The examination was performed in accordance with the standard protocol.

Following preprocedure assessment, informed consent was obtained. Conscious sedation was monitored by the radiology nursing section (see separate notes) monitored by the attending radiologist for 60 minutes. Vital signs, pre- and post-procedure monitoring were done by nurse in attendance with radiologists supervision. A transnasal intubation was done following a nasal drop of a local anesthetic.

Under fluoroscopic guidance, using guidewire and positional maneuvers, the enteroclysis catheter was advanced and the tip anchored at the distal horizontal duodenum.

Neutral enteral contrast was infused and monitored to a total of approximately 3.5 L. 0.6 mg Glucagon was administered IV prior to IV contrast administration. CT acquisition was done during continued infusion of enteral contrast following a 45 to 50 seconds delay. Intravenous administration of 100 ml lsovue 370 at 4 ml/second infusion rate. CT parameters used were 40 x 0.625 mm collimation reconstructed at 2 mm section thickness reconstructed at 1 mm intervals. The source images were transferred to an independent workstation (EBW) and cross referenced multiplanar interactive 2D interpretation was done by the radiologist. Images were reviewed using soft tissue window settings.

Following completion of the infusion, the catheter was withdrawn into the stomach and refluxed contrast removed prior to catheter removal.

No acute adverse events occurred.

Findings: There is no evidence of transmural inflammatory disease changes involving the small bowel or the colorectum. There is, however, mild prominence of the vasa recta in the right lower abdomen, mild increased attenuation of the cecum and ascending colon and adjacent distal small bowel. Suggest biopsy *at* the ascending colon to exclude microscopic colitis. If the patient has a history of blood in the stools, air double-contrast enteroclysis would be of value to exclude aphthous ileitis. CT enteroclysis may not be able to assess for early Crohn's until transmural involvement is seen. The rest of the colon also appears normal.

There are no fold changes to suggest adult celiac disease.

There is no evidence of a small bowel mass. The mesentery appears normal.

Solid abdominal organs are grossly unremarkable.

Impression:

1. No evidence of transmural inflammatory disease changes involving the small bowel or colorectum. No fold abnormalities to suggest sprue.

2. Prominence of vasa recta of cecum and ascending colon and distal ileum with question of mild increased attenuation. Consider microscopic colitis. See discussion and recommendation above.

If there is strong clinical suspicion of Crohn's disease, consider air DC barium entero-clysis to exclude or confirm early aphthoid changes.

3. Reproduction of abdominal pain during contrast infusion, thus, correlated for visceral hypersensitivity.

4. Solid abdominal organs grossly unremarkable.

What are the CPT® and ICD-9-CM codes reported?

Case 7

Location: Regional Hospital

Fluoro Hysterosalpingogram

Examination: Hysterosalpingogram (procedure performed by radiologist)

Indication: Infertility for 15 years. Patient had one child 15 years ago. Last menstrual period was 1/13/20XX.

No history of pelvic infection or surgery.

Comparison: None

Procedure: The examination and anticipated discomfort was discussed with the patient. A plastic vaginal speculum was introduced with the patient's legs in the stirrups following preliminary vaginal examination and lubrication. The posterior vaginal fornix and outer cervical os were prepped with a cleansing solution. A 5-F hysterosalpingogram catheter was used. The catheter balloon was inflated in the lower uterine segment. Fluoroscopic and radiographic assessments were done.

The patient tolerated the procedure well.

Findings: Contrast was administered through the catheter and multiple images were taken. There is a possible abnormal contour to the right cornua with patchy contrast opacification which may represent intramural contrast with intravasation.

No definite spillage of contrast from either fallopian tube was identified

Impression: 1. Possible right cornual contour abnormality manifested by focal extravasation and minimal intravasation of undetermined etiology. Recommend endovaginal ultrasound for further evaluation.

2. No contrast filling of either tubes and no spill into pelvic peritoneal space.

What are the CPT® and ICD-9-CM codes reported?

Case 8

Location: Regional Hospital

Exam:

Renal and bladder ultrasound dated 10/01/20XX

Renal artery Doppler evaluation dated 10/01/20XX

Comparison: Renal MRA dated 04/01/20XX

History: 80-year-old renal artery stenosis.

Findings: Multiple grayscale sonographic and color Doppler images of the kidneys and renal vasculature were submitted for interpretation.

The right kidney measures 10.1 cm without evidence of pelvic caliectasis.

There is a small 8 mm cyst noted within the lower pole of the right kidney. There is relatively normal internal architecture and echogenicity. The left kidney measures 10.4 cm with no evidence of pelvicaliectasis. There are at least 3 renal cysts identified, the largest measuring 2 cm in diameter. There is normal internal architecture and echogenicity. The bladder is distended with urine and appears within normal limits.

The aorta demonstrates peak systolic velocity of 1.07 m/sec.

The right renal artery origin demonstrates peak systolic velocity of 3.0 m/sec with a resistive index of 0.92. The midportion of the right renal artery demonstrates a peak systolic velocity of 1.1 m/sec with resistive index of 0.8. The right renal hilum has a peak systolic velocity of 0.64 m/sec with resistive index of 0.85. The inferior pole has a systolic velocity of 0.16 m/sec with resistive index of 0.54. The midpole has a systolic velocity of 0.18 m/sec and resistive index of 0.70.

The superior pole has a velocity peak of 0.22 m/sec the resistive index of 0.77.

The left renal artery origin demonstrates a peak systolic velocity of 2.0 m/sec with a resistive index of 0.87. The mid portion of the left renal artery demonstrates a peak velocity at 0.42 m/sec and a resistive index of 0.80. The left renal hilum has a peak systolic velocity of 0.47 m/sec and a resistive index of 0.82. The inferior pole has a systolic velocity of 0 16 m/sec and a resistive index of 0.67. The midpole has a systolic velocity of 0.17 m/sec and a resistive index of 0.63.

The superior pole has a velocity peak of 0.13 m/sec with a resistive index of 0.69.

Impression: Renal artery Doppler study:

1. Moderate stenosis of the right renal artery origin.

2. Mild to moderate left renal artery origin stenosis.

Renal and bladder ultrasound:

1. Bilateral probable renal cysts.
2. Normal appearing bladder

What are the CPT® and ICD-9-CM codes reported?

Case 9

Location: Regional Hospital

MRI of the lumbar spine

History: Low back pain.

Technique: On a 1.5 Tesla magnet multiple sagittal and axial images were performed through the lumbar spine using variable pulse sequences.

Findings: There is normal lumbar alignment. The conus is in normal position at the thoracolumbar junction. No suspect bone marrow lesions are present. There is mild anterior wedging of the L3 vertebral body. I am uncertain whether this is an acute or chronic finding.

At the T12–L1 level, there is a small posterior disc bulge. There is no central canal stenosis. There is no neural foraminal stenosis.

At the L1–L2 level, there is no disc bulge or protrusion. There is no central canal or neural foraminal stenosis.

At the L2–L3 level, there is moderate loss of disc height. There is 106s of T2 signal. There is a focal area of increased T1 signal involving the L2–L3 disc. This could be related to disc calcification or possibly blood product. There is a small posterior disc bulge. There is no central canal stenosis. There is no neural foraminal stenosis.

At the L3–L4 level, there is a minimal posterior disc bulge. There is no central canal stenosis. There is no neural foraminal stenosis.

At the L4–L5 level, there is mild loss of disc height and loss of T2 disc signal. There is a moderate size right paracentral disc protrusion impinging the anterior aspect of the thecal sac. There is no central canal stenosis. There is no neural foraminal stenosis.

At the L5–S1 level, there is no disc bulge or disc protrusion. There is no central or neural foraminal stenosis.

Impression: Mild anterior wedging of the L3 vertebral body. It is uncertain whether this is acute or chronic finding. There is increased T1 signal involving the L2–L3 disc which could be related to calcification or possible hemorrhage although this is felt to be less likely.

Moderate size right paracentral disc protrusion at L4–L5. Multilevel degenerative disc disease.

What are the CPT® and ICD-9-CM codes reported?

Case 10

Location: Regional Hospital

Type of procedure:

1. Abdominal aortic angiogram
2. Mesenteric artery angiogram

History: Mesenteric ischemia.

Informed consent: The procedure was discussed with the patient and his wife. The risks, including bleeding, infection, and vascular injuries such as dissection, perforation, thrombus, and embolus were outlined. Informed consent was obtained.

Contrast: 123 mL Ultravist 370.

Conscious sedation: Under continuous hemodynamic monitoring, 1 mg of Versed and 50 mcg of Fentanyl were given intravenously.

Description of procedure: The patient's right groin was sterilely prepped and draped. The skin and subcutaneous tissues were anesthetized with 2% lidocaine. The right common femoral artery was then percutaneously accessed and a wire advanced into the abdominal aorta under fluoroscopic visualization. A 5-French vascular sheath was placed into the right groin. An Omni Flush catheter was advanced to the upper abdominal aorta. Digital subtraction angiography of the abdominal aorta was performed. It demonstrates mild tortuosity of the aorta. The caliber is normal. A single renal artery is seen bilaterally without stenosis. The common iliac vessels are patent.

The Omni Flush catheter was then exchanged for a Cobra 2 catheter. The superior mesenteric artery was then selectively catheterized. Digital subtraction angiography was performed in multiple obliquities. The origin is patent. No focal stenosis or branch occlusions are identified. Next, the celiac artery was selectively catheterized. Digital subtraction angiography was performed in 2 obliquities. The origin is normal. No focal stenosis or branch occlusions are present.

Next, attempts were made to catheter the inferior mesenteric artery with the Cobra 2 catheter. This was unsuccessful. Selective catheterization of the inferior mesenteric artery was achieved with a Simmons 2 catheter. Digital subtraction angiography was then performed in 2 obliquities. The origin is patent. No stenosis or branch occlusions are present. The Simmons 2 catheter was removed as was the right groin sheath over a wire. Hemostasis in the right groin was then achieved using an Angio-Seal closure device.

Impression: Normal abdominal aortic angiogram and mesenteric angiogram of selective catheterization of the celiac, superior mesenteric and inferior mesenteric arteries.

What are the CPT® and ICD-9-CM codes reported?

Case 1

R/O MRSA—Central line catheter

Clinical Indications: Patient with fever not responsive to antibiotics

Collected: 03/30/XX 17:45   **Accession Num:** TXXXXX   **Status:** Authenticated

Method: Single nucleic acid sequence

Culture: Methicillin Resistant Staphylococcus aureus (MRSA) isolated

What are the CPT® and ICD-9-CM codes reported?

Case 2

Surgical pathology report: Requested by Dr. Steve Smith

Materials Received for Consultation, the pathologist is an employee of the lab

Two referred slides described as left deep cervical mass, left jugular lymph node

Clinical data: The slides are reviewed in conjunction with the patient being referred for care. Patient with complaints of new mass and extreme fatigue.

Final diagnosis:

Lymph node, left deep cervical mass, biopsy: Squamous cell carcinoma with basaloid features in fibrotic soft tissue possibly representing replaced lymph node.

Lymph node left deep internal jugular, biopsy. Sections show a central focus of a basaloid appearing squamous cell carcinoma within primarily fibrotic tissue likely representing a lymph node replaced by carcinoma. The carcinoma focally involves the inked margin of the specimen. An immunohistochemical stain for p16 performed at outside lab and reviewed by us reveals uniformly positive staining in the neoplastic cells.

Comment:

Per clinician request, EBV by in situ hybridization (FISH) is also performed

In situ hybridization report:

Deparaffinized sections are incubated with biotinylated cDNA probe to the EBER1 mRNA of Epstein-Barr virus. Localization is via a three step procedure employing mouse anti-biotin, biotinylated anti-mouse, and the avidin biotin complex using nickel chloride enhanced 3,3'-diaminobenzidine as chromogen. Results are listed below:

Block (Original label): A (AS10-3084) Population: Neoplastic cells

Label	Marker for	Results	Special Pattern or Comments
EBV PROBE	EBV probe, in situ hybridization	Negative	

Comment:

Lymph node, left deep cervical mass: No evidence of Epstein Barr Virus infection is identified within the neoplasm on in situ hybridization studies. The remainder of the above diagnosis remains unchanged.

What are the CPT® and ICD-9-CM codes reported?

Case 3

Requesting provider: CI, MD

Surgical pathology report: Collected: Received: 3/4/2011, the pathologist providing the service is an employee of the lab.

Materials received for consultation: Three referred specimens described as left base of tongue, left tonsil and right tonsil

Clinical data:
Slides are prepared and reviewed in conjunction with the patient being seen for Radiation Oncology consultation for carcinoma of base of tongue

Final diagnosis:
Eight slides prepared and reviewed A–H

Left base of tongue (part A) and right tonsil, biopsies (parts B, C, G): Squamous mucosa and tonsillar tissue; no carcinoma identified.

Left tonsil, biopsies (parts D, E, F, H): Tonsillar tissue with no carcinoma identified.

What are the CPT® and ICD-9-CM codes reported?

Case 4

Clinical Indications: The patient is a 28 y.o. female for routine lab tests.

Collected: 04/14/XX 13:29   Patient number:xxxxxxxxxxx   ID: verified

Site: right antecubital venipuncture   Disposition: outpatient, fasting

Tests: metabolic & CBC

Results:

Sodium Blood: 141 mEq/L (135–145)

Potassium Blood: 4.0 mEq/L (3.3–4.8)

Chloride Blood: 105 mEq/L (95–105)

Carbon Dioxide Blood: 24 mmol/L (23–30)

Urea Nitrogen Blood: 12 mg/dL (5–25)

Creatinine Blood: 0.86 mg/dL (0.70–1.50)

Glucose Blood: 93 mg/dL (70–110)

Calcium Blood (total): 9.3 mg/dL (8.5–10.5)

CBC: (automated)

WBC: 6.9 thou/uL (3.9–10.3)   **Hemoglobin Blood:** 14.5 g/dL (11.8–16.0)

Platelet Count: 235 thou/uL (135–370)   Red Blood Cells: 5.02 mil/uL (4.00–5.50)

Impression: normal labs

What are the CPT® and ICD-9-CM codes for the pathologist?

Case 5

Requested by R Simon, MD

Cytology report: Collected: 1/26/2011 Received: 1/27/2011, Pathologist performing the service is an employee of the lab.

Specimen source:
A. Peritoneal Fluid

Specimen description: 100 mls yellow fluid

Cytopreparation: 2 ccf

Pertinent clinical data and clinical diagnosis:
26-year-old female with end-stage renal disease (ESRD) due to type I diabetes presents for elective kidney transplant.

Cytologic impression:
Peritoneal dialysis drain fluid: No cytologically malignant cells are identified.

Comment: 100 mls yellow fluid is received from which two Papanicolaou stained cyto-centrifuged slides are made. Slides contain mesothelial cells with a spectrum of reactive changes and histiocytes. No malignant cells are identified.

What are the CPT® and ICD-9-CM codes?

Case 6

Requested by R Williams, MD

Surgical pathology report collected: 2/1/2011 Received: 2/2/2011. The pathologist is employed by the lab providing the service.

Clinical data: 26-year-old with end-stage renal (ESRD) disease due to type 1 diabetes, status post kidney, pancreas transplant with subsequent pancreas allograft removal, now with disseminated intravascular coagulation and decreased urine output and kidney allograft showing no flow to the kidney.

Description:
A) Received fresh designated "ureteral stent–gross only" is a 15 cm x 0.2 cm piece of plastic tubing with a 1.5 cm hairpin turn at either end. There are 0.05 cm holes at every 2 cm of the device.
B) Received fresh in a container labeled "removed kidney-gross and micro" is a 138 gram, 11 x 7 x 3 cm kidney. The specimen has a smooth, glistening, pink capsule with lightly adherent fibrous tissue. There are multiple surgical clips within the hilum and perihilar fat. The specimen is bivalved to reveal a sharp but irregular demarcation at the cortex and the medullary interface. No masses, nodules or lesions are grossly appreciated. There is probable intravascular thrombus. Representative sections are submitted as follows: B1—renal vein, renal artery and ureteral margins; B2–B5—representative sections of kidney parenchyma in relation to capsule.

Final diagnosis:
A) Medical device, removal: Pigtail catheter (gross only).
B) Kidney, allograft resection:
1. Widespread acute coagulative necrosis/infarct of renal parenchyma in the setting of multifocal microvascular thrombi (clinical history of disseminated intravascular coagulation).
2. Focal renal arterial thrombosis.
3. No evidence of humoral or cellular rejection.

What are the CPT® and ICD-9-CM codes?

Case 7

Clinical Indications: Inpatient day 32 in ICU with fever, hematuria, generalized edema, pneumonia

Urine **Fungal Culture:** Urine

Special Requests: None
Culture: No fungus isolated in 30 days

Lower Resp Fungal W/Dir. Exam: Sputum

Special Requests: None
Stain for Fungus: No fungi seen
Culture: One colony Candida albicans

Blood Fungal Culture: Blood Arm, Right

Special Requests: Aerobic bottle
Culture: No fungus isolated in 4 weeks

Blood Fungal Culture: Blood Right IJ Catheter SWAN

Special Requests: Aerobic bottle
Culture: No fungus isolated in 4 weeks

What are the CPT® and ICD-9-CM codes?

Case 8

Requested by D Freeman, MD
Surgical Pathology Report: Collected: 4/20/2011 Received: 4/20/2011. The pathologist providing the service is an employee of the lab.

Clinical Data: Post-heart transplant, rule out rejection.

Gross Description:
A) Received in a scant amount of formalin labeled "right ventricle endomyocardium" are seven tan-brown, irregular soft tissues averaging 0.1 cm in greatest dimension. The specimen is submitted in toto in cassette A1.
B) Received in a vial of immunofluorescence fixative labeled "right ventricle endomyo-cardium" are two tan, irregular soft tissues averaging 0.1 cm in greatest dimension. Specimen is entirely submitted for immunofluorescence.

Microscopic Description:
A) Sections of the paraffin-embedded material show six fragments of myocardium which are adequate to evaluate. There are few mononuclear cells present within the tissue, but these are beneath the threshold required to diagnose biologically mean-ingful rejection.

No cell injury is seen and no inclusion bodies are noted.

B) Sections of the frozen myocardium demonstrate two fragments of myocardium and one fresh blood clot. There is no inflammatory cell infiltrate.

Immunofluorescence Report:
Tissue, received in transport media, is washed in buffer and snap frozen in liquid nitrogen-cooled isopentane. Acetone-fixed frozen sections of the snap-frozen tissue are incubated with fluorescein-conjugated polyclonal antibodies to IgG, IgM, IgA, C3, C1q, fibrinogen, and albumin. Localization is thus via direct immunofluorescence. Indirect immunofluorescence staining of peritubular capillaries for C4d.

Results are as indicated below:

Block (Original Label): B Population: Microvascular endothelium

Label	Marker For	Results	Special Pattern or Comments
C4d	C4d (Quidel Clone A213), immunofluorescence	2+	Venule staining with high interstitial background

Block (Original Label): B1 Population: Microvascular endothelium

Label	Marker For	Results	Special Pattern or Comments
IgG IF	IgG, immunofluorescence	Negative	Interstitial staining
IgA IF	IgA, immunofluorescence	Negative	
IgM IF	IgM, immunofluorescence	2+	Capillary and venule staining
C3 IF	C3, immunofluorescence	2+	Venule staining
C1q IF	C1q, immunofluorescence	2+	Venule staining
FIB IF	Fibrinogen, immunofluorescence	Negative	Diffuse interstitial staining
ALB IF	Albumin, immunofluorescence	Negative	Diffuse interstitial staining

Final diagnosis:

A, B) Right ventricular endomyocardial biopsy:
1. No significant cellular rejection.
2. Immunofluorescence studies positive for humoral/vascular rejection (IgM and complement present). Please see comment.

Comment:

A, B) This is the fourth biopsy since transplant. Compared to his most recent biopsy, the current specimen shows no change in the degree of cellular rejection.

What are the CPT® and ICD-9-CM codes?

Case 9

Requested by P Norris, MD

Surgical Pathology Report

Materials received:
Referred slides of inguinal lymph node

Clinical data: History of Merkel cell carcinoma.

Final diagnosis:
Lymph node, left inguinal, excision:

1. High grade neuroendocrine carcinoma involving one of four lymph nodes (1/4); see Comment.
2. No extranodal extension identified.

Comment:
The neoplasm consists of sheets of small round blue cells with powdery chromatin, scant cytoplasm, and indistinct cell borders. Numerous mitotic figures and areas of single cell necrosis are seen. The morphologic findings are consistent with a high grade neuroendocrine carcinoma and the differential diagnoses include metastatic Merkel cell carcinoma or small cell carcinoma. Given the patient's reported history (slides not reviewed at UMMM), the features are consistent with metastatic Merkel cell carcinoma. Correlation with clinical findings is advised.

What are the CPT® and ICD-9-CM codes?

Case 10

Requested by D Smith, MD. The pathologist providing the service is an employee of the lab.

Surgical Pathology Report

Clinical data: Chronic infected skin ulcer status post amputation of first and third toes, current mid transmetatarsal amputation.

Gross description:
A) Received in formalin designated "right mid transmetatarsal amputation" is a distal right foot including second, fourth, and fifth toes, measuring 9.0 x 9.0 x 4.0 cm. Also in the container is a piece of tan bone measuring 2.4 x 1.3 x 1.3 cm. The skin and subcutaneous tissue recedes up to 4.0 cm from the smooth bony margins of resection. The skin is tan-white. The first and third toes are missing. The remaining toes are slightly flexed and with a thickened irregular nail of the second toe. There is a round, deep ulcer at the plantar surface of the foot proximal to the second toe, measuring 1.5 x 1.5 x 0.7 cm. No other lesions are identified. The piece of bone is submitted for decalcification. Representative sections are submitted in A1 and A2, including skin and soft tissue margins.

Final diagnosis:
A) Right foot, mid-transmetatarsal amputation:
1. Right foot with ulceration
2. Status post amputation of first and third toes.
3. Skin and soft tissue margins histologically viable.
4. Bone section pending decalcification, addendum report to follow.

Comment: Geographic fibrinoid necrosis associated with ulcer raises the possibility of a rheumatoid nodule.

Findings of decalcified specimen (A3).

Sections of the bone demonstrate chronic reactive changes. No evidence of active osteomyelitis is identified.

What are the CPT® and ICD-9-CM codes?

Case 1

Mark is a 45-year-old male and is here as a new patient to have several lipomas removed. He has had these for many years. He has had about 12 removed. They get bigger slowly over time. Some of them are tender to touch. They get irritated when he is handling people as a firefighter.

Past medical history: None.

Allergies: None.

Medications: None.

Past surgical history: Nasal surgery, knee surgery.

Social history: Cigarettes: None.

Family history: He does have a family history of melanoma in his paternal grandfather who died from it.

Physical examination: On examination, he has subcutaneous masses of his left forearm and two spots of his left posterior arm. That is the biggest of those three. It is about 1.3 cm. He has four on his right upper extremity, two on his lower forearm and two on his posterior arm. He has some on his belly.

Medical decision making: The patient has multiple lipomas, which are tender. He would like them removed. With his permission, I have drawn how we would incise the skin over these and about how long the scar would be. There is really no alternative to treatment other than surgery. Some plastic surgeons will do this with liposuction, but I have found that personally the recurrence rate is quite high when I have tried to do it with liposuction, so I generally just excise them. Risks would include infection and bleeding. We do not know why people get these, so this is something that Mark will have to deal with forever. We will do that here in the office. We will do about three at a time. We are going to start with his left upper extremity. It will be a privilege to take care of Mark.

What are the CPT® and ICD-9-CM codes reported?

99201

Case 2

Susan is a 67-year-old female and is referred by Dr. R with a suspicious neoplasm of her left arm. She has had it for about a year but it has grown a lot this last few months. I had the privilege of taking a skin cancer off her forearm in the past.

Past medical history: Hypertension, arthritis.

Allergies: None.

Medications: Benicar and Vytorin.

Social history: Cigarettes: None.

Physical examination: On examination, she has a raised lesion. It is a little bit reddish and is on her left proximal arm. It has a little bumpiness on its surface.

Medical decision making: Suspicious neoplasm, left arm.

My guess is this is a wart, but it may be a keratoacanthoma as Dr. R thinks it is. After obtaining consent, we infiltrated the area with 1 cc of 1% lidocaine with epinephrine, performed a 3 mm punch biopsy of the lesion, and then I shaved the rest of the lesion off and closed the wound with 3-0 Prolene. We will see her back next week to go over the results.

What are the CPT® and ICD-9-CM codes reported?

Case 3

Identification: The patient is a 37-year-old Caucasian lady.

Chief complaint: The patient is here today for follow-up of lower extremity swelling.

History of present illness: A 37-year-old with a history of dyslipidemia and chronic pain. The patient is here for follow-up of bilateral lower extremity swelling. The patient tells me the swelling responded to hydrochlorothiazide.

Exam: Very pleasant, NAD. Vitals: P: 67, R: 18, Temp 98.6, BP: 130/85.

Data review: I did review her labs, and echocardiogram. The patient does have moderate pulmonary hypertension.

Assessment:

1. Bilateral lower extremity swelling: This has resolved with diuretics, this may be secondary to problem #2.

2. Pulmonary hypertension: Etiology is not clear at this time, will do a work up and possible referral to a pulmonologist.

Plan: I think we will need to evaluate the etiology of the pulmonary hypertension. The patient will be scheduled for a sleep study.

What are the CPT® and ICD-9-CM codes reported?

992.2

729.8

416.8

Case 4

Age: 33 YRS—Established patient

Vital signs: TEMPERATURE: 98.9°F Tympanic, PULSE: 97 Right Radial, Regular, BP: 114/70 Right Arm Sitting, PULSE OXIMETRY: 98%, WEIGHT: 161 lbs

Current allergy list: Lortab

Current Medication List:

- Lunesta Oral Tablet 3 Mg, 1 Every Day at Bedtime, As Needed
- Prozac Oral Capsule Conventional 40 Mg, 1 Every Day
- Levothyroxine Sodium Oral Tablet 100 Mcg, 1 Every Day for Thyroid Meloxicam Oral Tablet 15 Mg, 1 Every Day For Joint Pain
- Imitrex Oral Tablet 100 Mg, 1 Tab Po As Directed, Can Repeat After 2 Hours, Max 2 Per Day Phenergan 25 Mg, 1 Every 4–6 Hours, As Needed For Nausea

Chief complaint: Here for a comprehensive annual physical and pelvic examinations.

History of present illness: Pt here for routine Pap and physical. Pt reports episode of syncope 2 weeks ago. Pt went to ER and had EKG, CXR and labs and says she was sent home and per her report everything was normal. She denies episodes since that time. She does occasionally have mild mid-epigastric discomfort but no breathing problems or light-headedness. Good compliance with her thyroid meds.

Past medical history: Depression.

Family history: No cancer or heart disease, mother has hypertension.

Social history: Tobacco Use: Currently smokes 1 1/2 PPD, has smoked for 15 to 20 years.

Review of systems: Patient denies any symptoms in all systems except for HPI.

Physical Exam:

Constitutional: Well developed, well nourished individual in no acute distress.

Eyes: Conjunctivae appear normal. PERRLA

ENMT: Tympanic membranes shiny without retraction. Canals unremarkable. No abnormality of sinuses or nasal airways. Normal oropharynx.

Neck: There are no enlarged lymph nodes in the neck, no enlargement, tenderness, or mass in the thyroid noted.

Respiratory: Clear to auscultation and percussion. Normal respiratory effort. No fremitus.

Cardiovascular: Regular rate and rhythm. Normal femoral pulses bilaterally without bruits. Normal pedal pulses bilaterally. No edema.

Chest/Breast: Breasts normal to inspection with no deformity, no breast tenderness or masses.

GI: Soft, non-tender, without masses, hernias or bruits. Bowel sounds are active in all four quadrants.

GU: external/vaginal: Normal in appearance with good hair distribution. No vulvar irritation or discharge. Normal clitoris and labia. Mucosa clear without lesions. Pelvic support normal.

Cervix: The cervix is clear, firm and closed. No visible lesions. No abnormal discharge. Specimens taken from the cervix for thin prep pap smear.

Uterus: Uterus non-tender and of normal size, shape and consistency. Position and mobility are normal.

Adnexa/Parametria: No masses or tenderness noted.

Lymphatics: No lymphadenopathy in the neck, axillae, or groin.

Musculoskeletal exam: Gait intact. No kyphosis, lordosis, or tenderness. Full range of motion. Normal rotation. No instability.

Extremities: Bilateral Lower: No misalignment or tenderness. Full range of motion. Normal stability, strength and tone.

Skin: Warm, dry, no diaphoresis, no significant lesions, irritation, rashes or ulcers.

Neurologic: CNS II-XII grossly intact.

Psychiatric: Mood and affect appropriate.

Labs/Radiology/Tests: The following labs/radiology/tests results were discussed with the patient: Alb, Bili, Ca, Cl, Cr, Glu, Alk Phos, K, Na, SGOT, BUN, Lipid profile, CBC, TSH, Pap smear.

Assessment/Plan:

Unspecified acquired hypothyroidism

What are the CPT® and ICD-9-CM codes reported?

Case 5

The patient is a 32-year-old male here for the first time.

Chief complaint: Left knee area is bothersome, painful moderate severity. The patient also notes swelling in the knee area, limited ambulation, and inability to perform physical activities such as sports or exercises. The patient first noticed symptoms approximately 4 months ago. Problem occurred spontaneously. Problem is sporadic. Patient has been prescribed hydrocodone and meloxicam. Patient has had temporary pain relief with the medications. The meloxicam has caused digestion problems so patient has avoided using it.

Past medical history: Patient denies any past medical problems.

Surgeries: Patient has undergone surgery on the appendix.

Hospitalizations: Patient denies any past hospitalizations that are noteworthy.

Medications: Hydrocodone

Allergies: Patient denies having allergies.

Family history: Mother: No serious medical problems; Father: No serious medical problems.

Social history: Patient is married. Occupation: Patient is a chef.

Review of Systems:

Constitutional: Denies fevers. Denies chills. Denies rapid weight loss.

Eyes: Denies vision problems.

Ears, Nose, Throat: Denies any infection. Denies loss of hearing. Denies ringing in the ears. Denies dizziness. Denies a sore throat. Denies sinus problems.

Cardiovascular: Denies chest pains. Denies an irregular heartbeat.

Respiratory: Denies wheezing. Denies coughing. Denies shortness of breath.

Gastrointestinal: Denies diarrhea. Denies constipation. Denies indigestion. Denies any blood in stool.

Genitourinary: Denies any urine retention problems. Denies frequent urination. Denies blood in the urine. Denies painful urination.

Integumentary: Denies any rashes. Denies having any insect bites.

Neurological: Denies numbness. Denies tremors. Denies loss of consciousness.

Hematologic/Lymphatic: Denies easy bruising. Denies blood clots.

Psychiatric: Denies depression. Denies sleep disorders. Denies loss of appetite.

Review of previous studies: Patient brings an MRI which is reviewed. Large knee effusion. No lateral meniscal tear. No ACL/PCL tear. No collateral fracture. Medial meniscus tear with grade I signal.

Vitals: Height: 6'0", Weight: 160

Physical examination: Patient is alert, appropriate, and comfortable. Patient holds a normal gaze. Pupils are round and reactive. Gait is normal. Skin is intact. No rashes, abrasions, contusions, or lacerations. No venous stasis. No varicosities. Reflexes are normal patellar. No clonus.

Knee: Range of motion is approximately from 5 to 100 degrees. Pain with motion. No localized pain. Negative mechanical findings. There is an effusion. Patella is tracking well. No tenderness. Patient feels pain especially when taking stairs or squatting.

Hip: Exam is unremarkable. Normal range of motion, flexion approximately 105 degrees, extension approximately 10 degrees, abduction approximately 25 degrees, adduction approximately 30 degrees, internal rotation approximately 30 degrees, external rotation approximately 30 degrees.

Neck: Neck is supple. No JVD.

Impression:
1. Synovitis of the left knee
2. Contracture of the left knee
3. Possible medial meniscal tear of right knee

Assessment and plan: A discussion is held with the patient regarding his condition and possible treatment options. Patient has GI upset. Patient is recommended to take Motrin 400 two to three times a day, discussion is held regarding proper use and precautions. Patient is given a prescription for physical therapy. We will obtain an MRI to rule out potential medial meniscus tear. Patient is instructed to follow up with PMD with labs. Patient is referred to Dr. XYZ. Patient may need arthroscopy if patient does have medial meniscus tear and repeat effusion.

What are the CPT® and ICD-9-CM codes reported?

Case 6

Established patient

Chief complaint: Thoracic spine pain

Problem List:

1. Rheumatoid arthritis.
2. Compression fracture of the thoracic spine T11.
3. Alcoholism.
4. Depression/anxiety.

Review of systems: His pain is significantly improved in his thoracic spine. He does have low back pain. He has a history of chronic low back pain. He is still wearing a thoracic support brace. He is going to follow up with Dr. X's office in about six weeks or so. Since I have seen him last he had a small flare of arthritis after his Humira injection. This resolved after 2–3 days. He had pain and stiffness in his hands. Currently he denies any pain and stiffness in his hands. He has one cystic mass on his left hand, second distal pad that is bothersome.

Current medications: Vasotec 20 mg a day, Folic Acid 1mg a day, Norvasc 5 mg a day, Pravachol 40 mg a day, Plaquenil 400 mg a day, Humira 40 mg every other week, Celexa 20 mg,a day, Klonopin .5 mg as needed, aspirin 81 mg a day, Ambien 10 mg as needed, Hydrocodone as needed.

Physical exam: He is alert and oriented in no distress. Gait is unimpaired. He is wearing the thoracic brace. Spine ROM is not assessed. Lungs: Clear. Heart: Rate and rhythm are regular.

Musculoskeletal exam: There is generalized swelling of the finger joints without any significant synovitis or tenderness. There is a cystic mass on the pad of his second left finger, which is tender. Remaining joints are without tenderness or synovitis.

Review of DEXA scan: (performed in office today) There is low bone density with a total T-score of -1.1 of the lumbar spine. Compared to previous it was -0.8. There has been a reduction by 3.6%. T-score of the left femoral neck -1.1, Ward's triangle -2.4, total T-score is -0.8 compared to previous there has been a 7% reduction from 2005.

Assessment:

1. Rheumatoid arthritis. He is doing fairly well. He does have a cystic mass, which seems to be a synovial cyst of the left second digit. He was wondering if he could have this aspirated.
2. Compression fracture and low bone density. He is being treated for osteoporosis because of this. He is tolerating Fosamax well. He is also using Miacalcin nasal spray temporarily to help with the pain and it seems to have been effective.

Plan:

1. Continue current therapy.
2. Aspirate the synovial cyst in the left second finger.
3. Follow up in about 6–8 weeks.
4. Repeat labs prior to visit.

Procedure note: With sterile technique and Betadine prep, the radial side of the second finger is anesthetized with 1 cc 1% Lidocaine for a distal finger block. Then the synovial cyst is punctured and material was expressed under the skin. I injected it with 10 mg of Depo-Medrol. He will keep it clean and dry. If it has any signs or symptoms of infection, he will let me know.

What are the CPT® and ICD-9-CM codes reported?

206.12
770.80
18

Case 7

XYZ Nursing Home

Subjective: The patient appears to be a little more altered than normal today. He is in some obvious discomfort. However, he is not able to communicate due to his mental status. Patient does appear fairly anxious.

Physical exam: Glucoses have been within normal limits. Patient has had poor p.o. intake, however, over the last 2–3 days. Temperature is 97, pulse is 79, respirations 20, blood pressure 152/92, and oxygen saturation 97% on room air. Patient is arousable. Extraocular movements are intact. Oral pharynx is clear. Lungs are clear to auscultation bilaterally. Heart has a regular rate and rhythm. Abdomen is nontender and nondistended. Patient is able to move all extremities. He does have some mild pain over the apex of his right shoulder and bruising over the lateral ribcage on the right side over approximately T8 to T10. No crepitus is noted. Patient indicates he hurts everywhere.

Ancillary studies: A.M. labs—none new this morning. X-ray shows no evidence of fracture with definitive arthritis. Patient has chronic distention of bowels. This is always atypical exam. Telemetry shows no significant new arrhythmias.

Assessment & Plan:

1. Patient is an 84-year-old Caucasian male who presented after a fall with rib contusion, right shoulder pain and uncontrolled pain since. He has been on Tramadol. However, I believe this is making him more altered. Thus, we will back of on medications and see if he comes back more to himself. We may try a different medication at a low dose later today if patient's mental status improves significantly. We will have patient out of bed three times a day. Physical therapy is working with the patient for significant deconditioning.

2. Patient with elevated blood pressures upon admission and still running a little bit high. Cardizem has been added to the medication regimen recently. We will follow this and see what it does for his blood pressure in the long run. He is in no immediate danger currently.

3. Very advanced dementia, will follow, continue on home medications.

4. Coronary artery disease and history of congestive heart failure. These appear stable at this time.

5. History of atrial fibrillation, sounds to be in regular rhythm currently and appears to be doing well on telemetry monitor. Again, cardizem has been added for better control and blood pressure control.

6. Type II diabetes mellitus. Glycemic control has been good. However, patient has had poor p.o. intake over the last 2–3 days, which may be due to pain. Thus, we will hold glipizide for now to prevent hypoglycemia.

7. We will follow the patient closely and adjust medications as necessary.

What are the CPT® and ICD-9-CM codes reported?

99309

Case 8

Hospital Admission

Chief complaint: Nausea, weakness

HPI: The patient is a 78-year-old Hispanic female with a history of diabetes, hypertension, and osteoporosis who was just discharged after hospitalization for gastroenteritis three days ago. She went home and was feeling fine, was tolerating regular diet until yesterday. She stated she feels nauseated, feels like she needs to throw up but cannot vomit. Her last bowel movement was yesterday. She stated it was diarrhea and states she has extreme weakness. No melena or hematochezia. No shortness of breath, no chest pain.

Medical history: Diabetes mellitus type 2. Hypertension. Osteoporosis.

Surgical history: None

Medicines: Benadryl 25 mg daily, Diovan 320/25 one daily, calcium 600 daily, vitamin C 500 daily, multivitamin 1 tablet daily, Coreg CR 20 mg daily, Lipitor 20 mg at bedtime, metform 1000 mg/day.

Allergies: Morphine

Social history: No tobacco, alcohol or drugs. She is a widow. She lives in Marta. She is retired.

Family history: Mother deceased after childbirth. Father deceased from asphyxia.

ROS: Negative for fever, weight gain, weight loss. Positive for fatigue and malaise.

Ears, Nose, Throat: Negative for rhinorrhea. Negative for congestion.

Eyes: Negative for vision changes.

Pulmonary: Negative for dyspnea.

Cardiovascular: Negative for angina.

Gastrointestinal: Positive for diarrhea, positive for constipation, intermittent changes between the 2. Negative for melena or hematochezia.

Neurologic: Negative for headaches. Negative for seizures.

Psychiatric: Negative for anxiety. Negative for depression.

Integumentary: Positive for rash for which she takes Benadryl.

Genitourinary: Negative for dysfunctional bleeding. Negative for dysuria.

Objective:

Vital signs: Show a temperature max of 98.1, T-current 97.6, pulse 62, respirations 20, blood pressure 168/65. O_2 sat 95% on room air. Accu-Chek, 135.

Generally: No apparent distress, oriented x 3, pleasant Spanish speaking female.

Head, ears, eyes, nose, throat: Normocephalic, atraumatic. Oropharynx is pink and moist. No scleral icterus.

Neck: Supple, full range of motion.

Lungs: Clear to auscultation bilaterally.

Cardiovascular: Regular rate and rhythm. No murmurs, gallops, rubs.

Abdomen: Soft, nontender, nondistended. Normal bowel sounds. No hepatospleno-megaly. Negative Murphy's sign.

Back: Costovertebral angle tenderness

Extremities: No clubbing, cyanosis or edema.

Laboratory Studies.

Shows a sodium 125, potassium 6.0, chloride 90, CO_2 27, glucose 103, BUN 13, creatinine 0.7, white count 8.3, hemoglobin and hematocrit 12.6, 37.1, platelets 195, 000. Differential shows 76% neutrophils. Amylase 42, CK-MB 1.7, troponin 0.05, CPK 59. PTT 26.9. PT and INR 12.9 and 1.09. UA shows 500 leukocyte esterase, negative nitrite, 15 of ketones, 10 to 25 WBCs.

Gallbladder sonogram shows a 1.24 x 1 cm echogenic focus in the gallbladder, possibly representing gallbladder polyp or gallbladder mass. CT abdomen and pelvis shows chole-lithiasis, small left pleural effusion, small indeterminate nodules both lung masses, no acute bowel abnormality and sclerotic appearance of right greater trochanter, no free air.

Assessment

1. Nausea, vomiting, diarrhea, likely gastroenteritis
2. Cystitis
3. Hypokalemia
4. Hyponatremia
5. Cholelithiasis
6. Diabetes mellitus type 2
7. Hypertension

Plan: Will admit patient for IV hydration, add Levaquin 500 mg IV q 24 hours. Will ad 20 mg KCl per L to IV fluid. Get a general surgery consult for cholelethiasis. Will check studies, fecal white blood cells, C. dif toxin and fecal stool culture and sensitivity.

What are the CPT® and ICD-9-CM codes reported?

796 2
294 70
414 0

Case 9

Hospital Progress Note

Subjective: Patient is without complaint. She states she feels much better. No vomiting or diarrhea. She did have bowel movement yesterday. No shortness of breath, no chest pain.

The patient and daughter were questioned again about her cardiac history. She denies any cardiac history. She has no orthopnea, no dyspnea on exertion, no angina in the past and she has never had any heart problems in the past.

Case discussed yesterday with Dr. Williams and I am waiting to find out on her surgery date.

Objective:

Vital signs: Shows a T-max of 99.6, T-current 98, pulse 72, respirations 18. Blood pressure 154/65, 02 sat 96% on room air. Accu-cheks, 113, 132, 96, 98.

General: No apparent distress, oriented x 3, pleasant English-speaking female.

Head, Ears, Eyes, Nose, Throat: Normocephalic, atraumatic. Oropharynx pink and moist. Left eye has sclera erythema. Pupils equal, round, and reactive to light accommodation.

Laboratory data: Shows C Dif toxin negative. Sodium 129, potassium 3.4, chloride 96, CO_2 27, glucose 72, BUN 12, creatinine 0.6. Urine culture positive for E. coli, sensitive to Levaquin.

Assessment:

1. Cholelithiasis
2. Cystitis
3. Conjunctivitis
4. Hyponatremia
5. Hypokalemia
6. Diabetes mellitus type 2
7. Hypertension

If the patient is not to go to surgery today, will feed the patient and likely discharge her if she tolerates regular diet. Will add Norvasc 5 mg p.o. daily. Also pleural effusion, small. Will repeat a chest X-ray PA and lateral this morning to evaluate that.

What are the CPT® and ICD-9-CM codes reported?

Case 10

Discharge Summary

Hospital course:

The patient was hospitalized two days ago with nausea and vomiting. She had an uneventful hospital course. She was diagnosed with cholelithiasis. General surgery was consulted. Dr. General thought this was perhaps causing her upper GI symptoms. She was scheduled for surgery on Monday. She was tolerating a regular diet. Her nausea and vomiting resolved and she desired to be dismissed home. She was found to have a bladder infection. She was started on Levaquin and she also had left eye conjunctivitis and she was given Ciloxan eye ointment for that.

Discharge Diagnoses:

1. Cholelithiasis
2. Cystitis
3. Conjunctivitis
4. Hyponatremia
5. Diabetes mellitus type 2
6. Hypertension

Discharge Medications:

1. Levaquin 500 mg p.o. daily x2 days
2. Ciloxan ointment, apply b.i.d.to left eye x 4 days/
3. Zofran 4 mg p.o. q. 4 hours p.r.n. nausea, vomiting #20
4. Benadryl 25 mg p.o. daily p.r.n. rash
5. Diovan 320 p.o. daily
6. Calcium 600 mg p.o. daily
7. Vitamin C 500 mg p.o. daily.
8. Metformin 1000 mg p.o. daily
9. Lipitor 20 mg p.o. at bedtime
10. Coreg CR 20 mg p.o. daily.

Discharge Diet: Cardiac

Activities: ad lib

Discharge instructions: Patient to be NPO after midnight Sunday.

Dismiss: Home

Condition: Good

Follow-up: Follow up with me in 1 week. Follow up on Monday morning for cholecystectomy. NPO after midnight on Sunday.

What are the CPT® and ICD-9-CM codes reported?

Case 1

A 10-year-old established patient presents today for well child check with mother with complaints of frequent urination during the day.

The patient has two sisters and sees dad sporadically. Lives in a smoke free environment. 1 dog, 1 rabbit.

Denies dysuria, abdominal pain, or rashes; all other systems are reviewed and negative.

Patient going into fourth grade with good grades. No parental concerns. Patient cooperates but does tend to back talk. Doing well on Concerta.

Exam

General: Normal

Head: Normal

Eyes: Normal

Ears: Normal

Nose: Normal

Mouth/throat: Normal

Neck: Normal

Abdomen: Normal

Rectal: Not examined

Genitals: Normal

Skin: 3 mm papule on dorsal R hand without disruption of creases

Urinalysis: Ketones, nitrite, leukocytes normal; trace blood, low specific gravity.

Counseled patient on the use of seat belts, bicycle/skate helmets, gun safety, water/sun safety.

Assessment: Well Child Check, ADHD, Wart, Frequent Urination

Refill Concerta 18 mg PO q AM

Wart cleansed with alcohol. Histofreeze x 25 seconds was performed to destroy the wart.

Varicella Vaccine #2 administered without any complications.

What are the CPT® and ICD-9-CM codes reported?

Case 2

Pre-procedure diagnosis: Asthma

Post-procedure diagnosis: Asthma

Procedure: Psychophysiological Therapy Biofeedback

The patient returned to clinic with daily diary documenting home peak flow readings and asthma symptoms. Diary was assessed and discussed with patient. Patient reports reduced dosing with inhaled steroids and fewer asthmatic episodes. Lungs and respiratory resistance assessed. Lungs clear, no wheezes or rhonchi noted.

HRV biofeedback was performed using a physiograph. ECG data were collected from the left arm and right leg, and were digitized at 510 Hz. EEG biofeedback equipment attached and baroreflex gain was assessed with beat-to-beat BP recordings and digitized at a rate of 252 samples per second. The sensor was placed on the participant's right middle finger, and the hand was elevated on a table to approximately the level of the heart.

Respiratory system impedance (Zrs) [between 2 and 32 Hz with 2-Hz increments] was measured using a pseudorandom noise forced oscillation system. It was presented in 40, 2-second bursts spaced equally throughout.

In order to minimize the effects of possible partial glottal closure during exhalation, each burst was triggered by the beginning of an inhalation.

Post procedure, inspirometer readings were recorded. Asthma symptoms were scored with the patient. Biofeedback procedure lasted approximately 28 minutes.

The patient is to return to clinic in two weeks with daily diary. It is expected the patient will continue with reduced regiment and asthmatic episodes.

What are the CPT® and ICD-9-CM codes reported?

Case 3

Performed in the office

Pre-procedure diagnosis: Gastroesophageal reflux disease (GERD), Heartburn

Post-procedure diagnosis: GERD

Procedure: Esophageal pH monitoring with Bravo pH Capsule

Pt was placed in supine position on examining bed, IV moderate sedation was administered. Visualization of esophagus with anatomic markers located during endoscopy. Endoscopy was removed and the Bravo pH Capsule delivery system was passed into the esophagus using the oral passage until the attachment site was obtained at approximately 5 cm proximal to the upper margin of the LES. The external vacuum pump was activated pulling the adjacent esophageal mucosa into the fastening well. Vacuum gauge at 600 mm Hg and held for 10 seconds.

The plastic safety guard on handle was then removed and the activation button was depressed and turned attaching the pH capsule to the esophageal wall. The activation button on handle was then twisted 90 degrees and re-extended, releasing the pH capsule. Esophagoscopy was repeated to verify capsule attachment.

Prior to procedure, the Bravo pH capsule was activated and calibrated by submersion in pH buffer solutions.

The patient tolerated the procedure well and was transferred into the recovery room.

The patient returned to the office two days later for download of the recording. The information was analyzed and interpreted.

What are the CPT® and ICD-9-CM codes reported?

Case 4

Pre-procedure diagnosis: Sleep Apnea

Post-procedure diagnosis: Obstructive sleep apnea

Procedure: Overnight Sleep Study

The 35-year-old patient in a Hospital Sleep Lab for attended, overnight polysomnogram. Patient oriented to room and changed into overnight clothing brought into lab by patient.

Latency to sleep onset slightly prolonged at 32.3 minutes. During the first 82 minutes of sleep, 80 obstructive apneas were manifested. The lowest SpO_2 during the non-supplemented sleep period was 73%. CPAP was then applied at 5 cm H2, and sequentially titrated to a final pressure of 18 cm H_2O. The Apnea-hypopnea index (AHI) changed from 60 events/hr to 4 events/hr. SpO_2 increased to 90%.

The sleep study with and without CPAP shows severe obstructive sleep apnea with improvement with CPAP settings at 18 cm H20. Based on the improved SpO_2 levels with CPAP, it is recommended this patient use a BIPAP machine during sleep hours due to obstructive sleep apnea events.

What are the CPT® and ICD-9-CM codes reported?

Case 5

Pre-procedure diagnosis: Aortic insufficiency; hypertension

Post-procedure diagnosis: Borderline Left Ventricular Hypertrophy, Mild Aortic Insufficiency, Left ventricular Ejection Fraction 80%

Procedure: 2D with M-mode Echocardiogram with pulsed continuous wave with spectral display and Doppler color flow mapping

Patient positioned in supine position on exam table.

Echocardiogram proceeded without incidence.

Findings:

1. Borderline left ventricular hypertrophy.

2. Mild aortic insufficiency.

3. Left ventricular ejection fraction 80%.

   What are the CPT® and ICD-9-CM codes reported?

Case 6

Pre-procedure diagnosis: Persistent Right and Left Leg pains; Extensive varicose vein disease

Post-procedure diagnosis: Varicose vein disease with inflammation, venous insufficiency, leg pains due to varicose veins

Procedure: Peripheral Vascular Duplex Ultrasound Evaluation of the Venous Anatomy of the Lower Extremities

Patient's right and left leg venous anatomy was examined in the standing position utilizing a B-Mode Duplex ultrasound machine with a 12 MHz probe. The focus was to determine the location and flow characteristics of both the deep and superficial venous systems. The evaluations included dynamically focused gray-scale and color imaging supplemented by Doppler spectroanalysis. Valsalva maneuver as well as calf and thigh compressions were performed to determine the patency and direction of blood flow, the exact paths of venous reflux in the major venous trunks, tributaries, and perforator veins. Ultrasonic mapping included images of major deep veins of the leg, saphenofemoral junction, the great saphenous vein above and below the knee, and the short saphenous vein system below the knee. Measurements and flow characteristics were obtained and listed on venous map in chart.

Bilaterally, the great saphenous veins were absent beginning at the saphenofemoral junction, due to previous surgery. Noted was venous reflux and enlargement of neovascular and tributary portions of the vein systems in the upper and lower legs. Abnormalities and associated perforator veins were documented on venous map in chart. The internal diameters of the leg varicosities varied to 5 and 3.8 mm in diameter, bilaterally. No evidence of deep venous reflux or thrombosis noted within the femoral, popliteal, gastrocnemius, or posterior tibial vessels. Photocopies were taken of the venous abnormalities and are included in the medical record.

Findings:

1. Varicose vein disease with inflammation

2. Venous insufficiency

3. Leg pains due to varicose veins

What are the CPT® and ICD-9-CM codes reported?

Case 7

Pre-procedure diagnosis: Excessive Daytime Sleepiness, Snoring, Epworth Score 18

Post-procedure diagnosis: Sleep Study

Procedure: Polysomnogram, attended

This 25-year-old patient underwent overnight polysomnogram with the recording of EEG, EOG, submental and anterior tibialis EMG, respiratory effort, nasal and oral airflow, EKG, continuous pulse oximetry. Total time in bed of 386 minutes and a total of sleep time of 221 minutes. The sleep latency was 24 minutes and the REM sleep latency was 18 minutes. Throughout the night, the patient had a total of 256 episodes of arousals and 6 awakenings. Sleep efficiency was 56%. No apparent parasomnia noted. The average oxygen saturation was reported to be 95% with the lowest saturation being 84%. There were no periodic leg movements for an Index of 0.0 and cardiac arrhythmias were not present.

Impression: Mild sleep apnea

What are the CPT® and ICD-9-CM codes reported?

Case 8

Pre-procedure diagnosis: Epilepsy with history of seizures, VNS Implant

Post-procedure diagnosis: Epilepsy with history of seizures, VNS Implant

Procedure: Vagal Nerve Stimulator Analysis

Patient here for VNS implant analysis with possible adjustments.

The programming head was placed over the implanted neurostimulator located within the patient's neck-left side. Impedance was verified insuring parameters within normal limits. Parameters charted on flowchart within medical record. Operating status of neurostimulator reflects "on". Estimated time for analysis/interrogation was 20 minutes in duration.

Patient denies questions at this time. Will repeat analysis in three months.

What are the CPT® and ICD-9-CM codes reported?